Jane's World Sailplanes

and Motor Gliders / *Andrew Coates*

New edition

Jane's Publishing Company
London · Sydney

Printed in Great Britain by
Netherwood Dalton & Co Ltd

Designed by Paul Minns

ISBN 0 7106 0017 8

Contents

Photograph credits

The complete history of gliding is impossible to relate in a few short sentences. For centuries man had dreamed of spreading his wings and soaring like a bird but it was not to be until the closing years of the nineteenth century that experimenters like Otto Lilienthal in Germany and Octave Chanute in the USA first succeeded in cheating gravity – if only for a short time – in their crude and dangerous hang-gliders. But credit for building the first true controlled glider must go to the acknowledged pioneers of powered flight, Orville and Wilbur Wright, who made numerous flights over the sand dunes at Kitty Hawk, North Carolina, in their 1902 glider.

By the mid-1920s, pilots were regularly returning flight times measured in hours, generally by using the up-currents around hills to slope-soar. It was not long, however, before they learned how to use thermals to gain the height necessary for cross-country flying. Most of this pioneering work was done in Germany, a country with a particularly strong gliding movement centred at the *Wasserkuppe* in the Rhön district. In fact, most of the credit for early aerodynamic advances in sailplane design must go to the German Akafliegs which, by the mid-1939s, were designing streamlined cantilever-winged aircraft with enclosed cockpits and long tapered wings, the forebears of today's sailplanes.

The Second World War forced something of a recession on the development of gliding as a sport and the machines of the 1950s were little different from those of the pre-war years, although there were a few war-surplus training gliders about. The great revolution in sailplane design and construction was to come about in the 1960s with the marriage of special laminar-flow wing sections to glassfibre as a building material. Glassfibre confers great structural strength for relatively low weight and has the added advantage of being extremely smooth, essential where drag has to be kept to a minimum. It is also quite easy to work, and several amateur-built sailplanes use glassfibre as the prime material. Thus, by the end of that decade, sailplanes had evolved into sleek, comfortable machines, often of great beauty, capable of phenomenal performance, yet with handling characteristics that made them as safe to fly for relatively inexperienced sport pilots as for the most dedicated competition fliers.

But sailplane design has not stood still and the last decade has witnessed some startling advances in the quest for better and better performance. The modern competition machine can incorporate an impressive array of performance aids, ranging from camber-changing flaps on the wing trailing edge, which can be drooped to provide extra drag for landing or cranked up marginally to reduce drag for high-speed cross-country flying between thermals, to water ballast tanks in the wings which increase the gross weight and aid penetration. The number of pilots completing flights of more than 1,000 km (620 ml) has increased dramatically; of the 33 FAI Diplomas awarded, twelve have been claimed since the beginning of 1976.

Not all gliding is competitive of course, and large numbers of people fly simply for the sheer pleasure of it all. Their aircraft tend to be less aerodynamically advanced and usually more spartan in their equipment; these gliders form the bulk of the 191 types described in this book. Drawn from twenty nations, they embrace historic pre-war gliders as well as a number of experimental 'one-off' and home-built designs. Also included are a number of motor gliders, a relatively new breed of aircraft that has evolved through the need to dispense with the ground-crew and launching aids necessary for conventional glider operations.

For convenience, the contents have been divided alphabetically by country, and each entry consists of a short technical description, table of data and both a specially prepared three-view drawing and a photograph.

The author would like to acknowledge the valuable help which has been received from many different sources all over the world, and from the many friends, both personal and in gliding clubs and the sailplane industry, without whom this book could not have been compiled. Thanks are due to Mrs G. Bryce-Smith, Editor of *Sailplane and Gliding*, the official journal of the British Gliding Association; Mrs R. Harwood, Mr C. Wills and John Taylor of *Jane's All the World's Aircraft* for the loan of photographs, and to the many individual photographers credited at the front of this book; and not least to my Editor, Paul Ellis, for all his help.

Andrew Coates ARAeS
Hertfordshire
April 1978

Introduction to new edition

Jane's World Sailplanes and Motor Gliders, first published in 1978, has been substantially revised and updated to produce this edition. Seventeen new aircraft are included, drawings have been amended to take account of modifications to existing types, and there are many new photographs.

Edmund Schneider, who built the Grunau Baby in Germany and was one of the pioneer sailplane manufacturers, was invited by the Gliding Federation of Australia to set up a sailplane factory in Australia after the Second World War. He first produced the Kangaroo two-seater, which flew in 1953, followed by the Grunau Baby 4, the Kookaburra, Nymph, Kingfisher, Arrow and Boomerang.

The ES 52 Kookaburra is a two-seat trainer and is used by the majority of Australian gliding clubs. The original Kookaburra first flew in 1952, and the ES 52B in 1959. The model B is an improved version with the wing span increased from 11.7 m (38 ft 4½ in) to 14.86 m (48 ft 9 in), and is fitted with a nose wheel instead of a skid to ease ground handling. The cockpit has been enlarged and a wheel-brake is incorporated.

The fuselage is constructed from plywood-covered wooden frames and stringers. The one-piece blown canopy is hinged aft and there is a window on each side under the wing root to improve visibility. The three-piece wing is of conventional wooden construction with two spars. The aircraft is semi-aerobatic.

Data ES 52 Kookaburra
Manufacturer Schneider
First flight June 1954
Wing span 11.7 m (38 ft 4½ in)
Length 7.9 m (25 ft 11 in)
Height 1.38 m (4 ft 6½ in)
Wing area 15.0 m² (161.5 sq ft)
Wing section Göttingen 549/M-12
Aspect ratio 9.13
Empty weight 220 kg (485 lb)
Max weight 393 kg (866 lb)
Water ballast None
Max wing loading 26.2 kg/m² (5.36 lb/sq ft)
Max speed 119 kt (220 km/h)
Stalling speed 36 kt (67 km/h)
Min sinking speed at 39 kt (72 km/h) 1.05 m (3.4 ft)/sec
Max rough air speed 81.5 kt (151 km/h)
Best glide ratio at 44 kt (81 km/h) 20

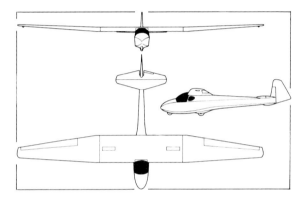

Australia / **Schneider ES 60B Super Arrow**

The Super Arrow is a single-seat Standard Class sailplane designed by Harry Schneider, son of the late founder of the company. The ES 60B Super Arrow, which first flew in September 1969, is a development of the ES 59 Arrow, which was commissioned by the Gliding Federation of Australia. The ES 60B is identical to the ES 60 Boomerang, designed in 1964 for competition flying, except for the tail unit. The boomerang-shaped all-flying tailplane of the ES 60, positioned one third up the fin, has been replaced on the ES 60B by a conventional tailplane and elevator located at the base of the fin.

The unusual feature of the ES 59 Arrow is that the wing is constructed in one piece, wingtip to wingtip. It consists of a moulded plastic leading edge with birch plywood covering back to 60% chord. Metal Schempp-Hirth airbrakes are fitted. The fuselage is a ply-covered semi-monocoque structure with glassfibre fairings and features a non-retractable landing wheel with brake. The cockpit is lined and the canopy is hinged sideways. An adjustable back-rest and rudder pedals are incorporated.

Data ES 60B Super Arrow
Manufacturer Schneider
First flight September 1969
Wing span 15.0 m (49 ft 2½ in)
Length 7.04 m (23 ft 1 in)
Height 1.52 m (5 ft 0 in)
Wing area 12.87 m² (138.6 sq ft)
Wing section Wortmann FX-61-184/60-126
Aspect ratio 17.5
Empty weight 221.5 kg (488 lb)
Max weight 347 kg (765 lb)
Water ballast None
Max wing loading 26.96 kg/m² (5.52 lb/sq ft)
Max speed 121 kt (225 km/h)
Stalling speed 32.5 kt (60 km/h)
Min sinking speed at 40 kt (75 km/h) 0.7 m (2.3 ft)/sec
Max rough air speed 89 kt (165 km/h)
Best glide ratio at 49 kt (90 km/h) 31

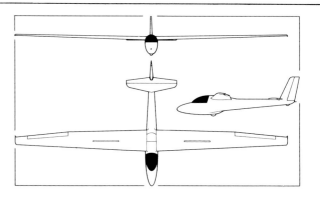

Sutherland MOBA-2C / Australia

In 1972 the MOBA-2A, designed by an aircraft engineer, Gary Sutherland, was one of the two winners of an Australian Gliding Federation competition to design a 13 m (42 ft 8 in) sailplane which could be built in a small workshop with limited tools. The MOBA-2C is an improved version of the 15 m MOBA-2B. There is less emphasis on cheapness in the design of the MOBA-2C, resulting in a versatile and ambitious sailplane.

The fuselage, of the elongated pod and boom type, is an all-metal semi-monocoque structure, with a unique glassfibre cockpit shell which, with the canopy, slides forward on rollers and tracks to provide access to the cockpit.

Armrests are provided and the control column is side-mounted.

The high-set three-piece wings and T-tail are of mixed construction, with aluminium box-section spars, plywood ribs, plastic foam and glassfibre skins. The flaps are of aluminium but the ailerons, tailplane and elevator are of wood. The landing gear consists of a retractable monowheel and a tailwheel.

Still under construction in 1979, the prototype was expected to make its first flight that year.

Data MOBA-2C
Manufacturer Gary Sutherland
First flight 12 December 1979
Wing span 15.0 m (49 ft 2½ in)
Length 6.78 m (22 ft 3 in)
Height 1.32 m (4 ft 4 in)
Wing area 9.08 m² (97.7 sq ft)
Wing section Wortmann FX-67-K-150
Aspect ratio 24.74
Empty weight 226 kg (499 lb)
Max weight 331 kg (730 lb)
Max wing loading 36.5 kg/m² (7.48 lb/sq ft)
Max speed 105 kt (194.5 km/h)
Stalling speed 42 kt (78 km/h)
Min sinking speed at 45 kt (83 km/h) 0.61 m (2.0 ft)/sec
Max rough air speed 88 kt (163 km/h)
Best glide ratio at 50 kt (93 km/h) 37

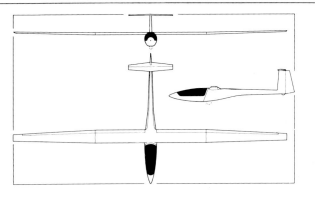

Austria / **Alpla-Werke AVo 68 Samburo**

The Samburo is a low-wing motor glider designed for training, cross-country and recreational flying. It was designed by Werner Vogel with help from Prof. Dr. Ernst Zeibig of Vienna and built at the recently established glider department of the Alpla-Werke. It has a fabric-covered steel-tube frame fuselage and conventional tail. The aft section of the large two-piece canopy slides back to provide access over the wing. The wings are of wood and fabric construction and incorporate spoilers. They fold to 10 m (32 ft 9½ in) for hangarage.

Seating is side-by-side and dual controls are provided. The landing gear includes a fixed main wheel, steerable tail wheel and small wing support wheels on nylon legs. The main wheel brake can also be used as a parking brake.

The Limbach engine is situated in the nose and drives a two-blade variable-pitch propeller. The AVo 60 is a lighter variant powered by a 60 hp engine driving a fixed pitch propeller. It uses less fuel and has a smaller fuel tank. Performance is similar to that of the AVo 68 with the exception of a slower rate of climb.

Sixteen Samburos had been built by the end of 1977.

Data   AVo 68
Manufacturer   Alpla-Werke
First flight   1971
Wing span   16.7 m (54 ft 9½ in)
Length   7.9 m (25 ft 11 in)
Height   1.82 m (5 ft 11½ in)
Wing area   20.7 m² (222.8 sq ft)
Wing section   Göttingen 549/NACA 64$_2$
Aspect ratio   13.6
Empty weight   470 kg (1,036 lb)
Max weight   685 kg (1,510 lb)
Water ballast   None
Max wing loading   31.4 kg/m² (6.43 lb/sq ft)
Max speed   92 kt (170 km/h)
Stalling speed   32.5 kt (60 km/h)
Min sinking speed at 40 kt (74 km/h)   0.85 m (2.79 ft)/sec
Best glide ratio at 43 kt (80 km/h)   24
Power plant   Limbach, 60 hp

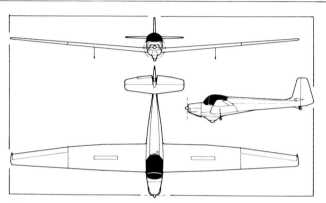

T-O run   150-180 m (492-590 ft)
Rate of climb   2.8 m (9.2 ft)/sec

H.W. Brditschka of Linz, Austria, currently produces two powered sailplanes, the single-seat HB-3 and the larger two-seat HB-21.

The wing of the HB-3 is based on the design of Ing. Fritz Raab for the Krähe sailplane and is constructed from red pine, spruce and birch ply. The HB-3 is suitable for training and for flying in mountainous terrain, having a short take-off run and good rate of climb. Three prototypes were built, the first of which flew in June 1971.

This unusual motor glider has a cantilever all-wood high wing, all-wood ailerons and upper-surface spoilers. The fuselage consists of a steel-tube frame with glassfibre covering. The tail unit is joined to the fuselage by two steel tubes, the lower one running below the propeller to the base of the fuselage and the upper one running through the centre of the propeller. The structure is wire-braced. The Rotax 642 two-stroke engine drives a Hoffmann two-blade fixed-pitch propeller via a belt.

In 1973 an HB-3 became the first self-launching glider to be electrically powered. This version, known as the MB-E1, uses one 8-10 kW (13 hp) Bosch electric motor.

Data HB-3BR
Manufacturer Brditschka
First flight June 1971
Wing span 12.0 m (39 ft 4½ in)
Length 7.0 m (22 ft 11½ in)
Height 2.95 m (9 ft 8 in)
Wing area 14.22 m² (153.1 sq ft)
Wing section Göttingen 758/Clark Y
Aspect ratio 11.1
Empty weight 255 kg (562 lb)
Max weight 372 kg (820 lb)
Water ballast None
Max wing loading 26.2 kg/m² (5.36 lb/sq ft)
Max speed 95 kt (175 km/h)
Stalling speed 32.5 kt (60 km/h)
Min sinking speed 1.15 m (3.8 ft)/sec
Best glide ratio at 43 kt (80 km/h) 21
Power plant Rotax 642 2-stroke, 30.6 kW (41 hp)

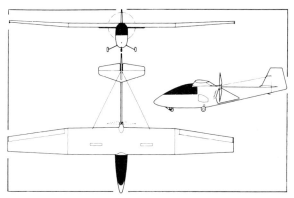

T-O run 100 m (328 ft)
Rate of climb at S/L 180 m (590 ft)/min
Range 700 km (378 nm)

Austria / **Brditschka HB-21**

The HB-21 is a two-seat development of the HB-3 motor glider (page 13) and has the same arrangement of propeller allowing the upper tail boom to pass through the propeller boss.

The three-piece wings are constructed from birch ply with laminated beech spars and incorporate wooden ailerons and upper-surface spoilers. The tail is of conventional wooden construction with fabric-covered control surfaces. The fuselage is similar to that of the HB-3 but is of increased length. It consists of a tubular steel frame with glassfibre covering and incorporates a roomy heated cockpit with two seats set in tandem, covered by a high-domed three-piece

canopy hinged to open sideways.

As with the smaller HB-3 a choice of power units is available: the HB-21L is powered by a 48.5 kW (65 hp) VW-Westermayer 1600G flat-four; the HB-21R uses a 30.6 kW (41 hp) Rotax 642 flat-twin engine, either driving a Hoffmann HO 14-175 B 117 LD two-blade fixed-pitch propeller. A 54 litre (11.9 Imp gallon) aluminium fuel tank is situated in the wing.

Twelve HB-21s had been sold by early 1978. One took part in the Sixth German Motor Glider Competition in 1976.

Data HB-21R
Manufacturer Brditschka
First flight 1973
Wing span 16.24 m (53 ft 3½ in)
Length 7.9 m (25 ft 11 in)
Height 2.6 m (8 ft 6¼ in)
Wing area 18.98 m² (204.3 sq ft)
Wing section Wortmann FX-61-184/60-126
Aspect ratio 13.9
Empty weight 418 kg (922 lb)
Max weight 640 kg (1,411 lb)
Water ballast None
Max wing loading 33.7 kg/m² (6.9 lb/sq ft)
Max speed 140 kt (260 km/h)
Stalling speed 35.5 kt (66 km/h)
Min sinking speed at 43 kt (80 km/h) 0.8 m (2.6 ft)/sec
Best glide ratio at 54 kt (100 km/h) 28
Power plant Rotax 642 2-stroke, 30.6 kW (41 hp)

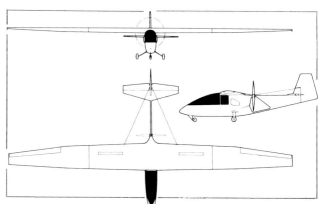

T-O run 170 m (558 ft)
Rate of climb at S/L 132 m (433 ft)/min
Range 650 km (350 nm)

Oberlerchner Mg 19 / Austria

After the Second World War, Austrian industrialist Joseph Oberlerchner promoted the re-establishment of sailplane manufacture and was responsible for producing the Mg 19, a development of the pre-war Mg 9.

Ing. Erwin Musger, designer of the Mg series, had established and sustained pre-war Austria as a significant producer of sailplanes. His first design, the Mg 2, appeared in 1930 and was a cantilever shoulder-wing glider with gull wings spanning 18 m (59 ft 0½ in). It was followed in 1931 by the Mg 4, the first Austrian high performance glider, which gave rise to a series of appreciable distance flights. A later development was the Mg 10.

In 1935 Musger designed the two-seat Mg 9, in which he set up the Austrian duration record of 8.09 hours in 1936. On 10 September 1938 a world duration record of 40 hours 51 minutes was established, also in an Mg 9. The Mg 12 training glider was produced just before the outbreak of war. The Mg 19 itself is a two-seat tandem trainer with a low-set gull wing of conventional wood and fabric construction. The prototype flew for the first time in November 1951, and many of this successful and popular trainer were built and are still flying.

Data Mg 19a
Manufacturer Josef Oberlerchner
First flight November 1951
Wing span 17.6 m (57 ft 9 in)
Length 8.04 m (26 ft 4½ in)
Height 1.65 m (5 ft 6 in)
Wing area 21.0 m² (226.1 sq ft)
Wing section Göttingen 549/676
Aspect ratio 14.2
Empty weight 298 kg (657 lb)
Max weight 480 kg (1,058 lb)
Water ballast None
Max wing loading 22.9 kg/m² (4.69 lb/sq ft)
Max speed 97 kt (180 km/h)
Stalling speed 27 kt (50 km/h)
Min sinking speed at 33.5 kt (62 km/h) 0.65 m (2.1 ft)/sec
Max rough air speed 70 kt (130 km/h)
Best glide ratio at 36 kt (67 km/h) 27.8

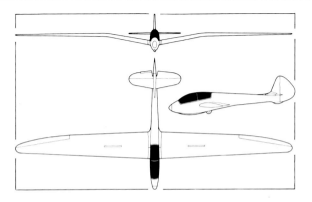

Austria / **Oberlerchner Mg 23**

Experience gained with the successful Mg 19 (page 15) was used by Erwin Musger in designing the high performance Mg 23, which first flew in June 1955.

The Mg 23 is a single-seat sailplane of conventional plywood construction. It has single-spar wooden wings with the spar set well behind the leading edge and layers of plywood stiffening forward of the spar. This and the close rib spacing of 125 mm (5 in) facilitate production of smooth polished surface areas. The wings are fitted with wooden Schempp-Hirth airbrakes.

The fuselage consists of a plywood shell with a reinforced nose and a Plexiglas canopy.

The landing gear consists of a single wheel with brake, a nose skid which uses rubber to provide a certain amount of shock absorption, and a bow-shaped tail skid.

The Mg 23 repeated the success of the Mg 19 by winning the Austrian State Championships and improving upon a number of national records. It was also a landmark in that it signalled the start of the Austrian national team and helped establish Austria among the contenders to be reckoned with in World Championships.

The last sailplane to be built by Josef Oberlerchner was the Mg 23 SL (described below), which appeared in 1962 with a taller fin, longer canopy and lowered landing wheel.

Data Mg 23 SL
Manufacturer Josef Oberlerchner
First flight April 1962
Wing span 16.4 m (53 ft 9½ in)
Length 7.11 m (23 ft 4 in)
Wing area 14.21 m² (153 sq ft)
Wing section NACA 63₁315
Aspect ratio 18.54
Empty weight 240 kg (529 lb)
Max weight 360 kg (794 lb)
Water ballast None
Max wing loading 25.3 kg/m² (5.18 lb/sq ft)
Max speed 119 kt (220 km/h)
Stalling speed 32.5 kt (60 km/h)
Min sinking speed at 37 kt (68 km/h) 0.66 m (2.2 ft)/sec
Max rough air speed 70 kt (130 km/h)
Best glide ratio at 42.5 kt /79 km/h) 32

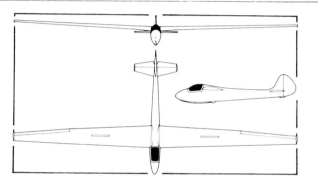

The standard Austria, which won the 1960 OSTIV prize for the best Standard Class sailplane, was commissioned by the Austrian Aero Club. The designer, Rüdiger Kunz, was aiming to produce a sailplane with a relatively low wing loading and a high lift/drag ratio, and consequently had to devise a completely new method of construction.

The Standard Austria is built entirely of wood with the exception of the nose section, the pilot's seat and the tail-cone, all of which are glassfibre. The large fixed landing wheel with its disc brake is situated in front of the centre of gravity. The wood-and-fabric V-tail is all-moving and incorporates geared tabs. The wooden wing is of stressed-skin construction without spars and is fabric covered from 65% chord to the trailing edge.

The great strength of this high performance sailplane, together with its good flying characteristics, make the Standard Austria especially suitable for cloud flying.

The 1964 version of the Standard Austria, the model SH, was fitted with a new wing with an Eppler 266 wing section. This modification improves performance at speeds between 32 and 54 kt (60 to 100 km/h).

Data Standard Austria
Manufacturer Austrian Aero Club
First flight July 1959
Wing span 15.0 m (49 ft 2½ in)
Length 6.2 m (20 ft 4 in)
Wing area 13.5 m² (145.3 sq ft)
Wing section NACA 65₂415
Aspect ratio 16.7
Empty weight 205 kg (452 lb)
Max weight 323 kg (712 lb)
Water ballast None
Max wing loading 23.93 kg/m² (4.9 lb/sq ft)
Max speed 135 kt (250 km/h)
Stalling speed 30 kt (55 km/h)
Min sinking speed at 37.5 kt (70 km/h) 0.7 m (2.3 ft)/sec
Max rough air speed 75.5 kt (140 km/h)
Best glide ratio at 56.5 kt (105 km/h) 34

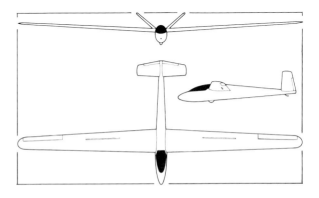

Brazil / **EEUFMG CB-2 Minuano**

The Brazilian gliding movement operates under somewhat difficult conditions not only because of the geography of the country but also because poor roads hamper retrieval. This, added to the country's distance from the main centres of sailplane manufacture, has contributed to the patchwork development of the sport. Nevertheless, there have been several indigenous designs, among them the Quero Quero II, the two-seat Neiva and the CB-2 Minuano.

The Minuano was designed by Professor Claudio Barros and built at the Air Research Centre of Engineering at Minhas Gerais University. Construction started in 1971 and the aircraft first flew on 20 December 1975.

A single-seat high performance sailplane, the Minuano has cantilever high-set wings utilising a single aluminium spar. The covering is a plywood/glassfibre honeycomb sandwich. The plain flaps and ailerons are of similar construction. There are no airbrakes but the flaps deflect up to 90°. The fuselage consists of an all-wood semi-monocoque structure. The unsprung monowheel landing gear is manually retractable.

Data CB-2 Minuano
Manufacturer EEUFMG (CEA)
First flight December 1975
Wing span 15.0 m (49 ft 2½ in)
Length 7.0 m (22 ft 11½ in)
Height 1.43 m (4 ft 8¼ in)
Wing area 10.2 m² (109.8 sq ft)
Wing section Wortmann FX-61-163/60-126
Aspect ratio 22.0
Empty weight 214 kg (472 lb)
Max weight 304 kg (670 lb)
Water ballast None
Max wing loading 29.8 kg/m² (6.1 lb/sq ft)
Max speed 140 kt (260 km/h)
Stalling speed 35 kt (65 km/h)
Min sinking speed at 39 kt (72 km/h) 0.55 m (1.8 ft)/sec
Max rough air speed 86.5 kt (160 km/h)
Best glide ratio at 48.5 kt (90 km/h) 38

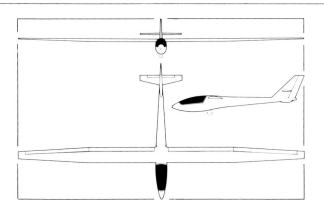

The best known Brazilian-built sailplane outside its native country is the Urupema, which took part in the 1968 World Championships at Leszno and in those of 1970 at Marfa, Texas, where it was placed twenty-second out of forty competitors in the Standard class.

The design of this 15-metre high performance single-seat sailplane was started in 1964 by a group of engineers and students at the Centro Tecnico de Aeronautica (CTA) under the leadership of Guido Pessotti. This group also work on powered aircraft and were responsible for the 8-metre Periquito 2 sailplane in 1956.

This long-nosed glassfibre and wood built sailplane has cantilever shoulder wings, with a forward sweep of 1° 22′ at quarter chord, which incorporate DFS airbrakes. The fuselage is a semi-monocoque wooden structure with a very low ground incidence. The conventionally sited tail assembly incorporates an all-moving tailplane with anti-balance tabs. Like the wings, construction is of wood and honeycomb paper sandwich. The pilot is seated in a reclining position in a long slim cockpit reminiscent of the Foka, and covered by a one-piece clear detachable canopy. The cockpit features adjustable rudder pedals, head rest, thigh support and ventilation system. Landing gear consists of a non-retractable wheel with brake.

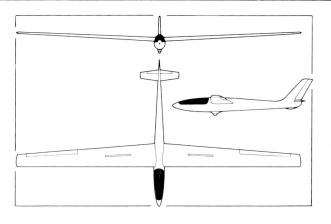

Data 6505 Urupema
Manufacturer IPD/PAR
First flight January 1968
Wing span 15.0 m (49 ft 2½ in)
Length 7.45 m (24 ft 5¼ in)
Height 1.52 m (4 ft 11½ in)
Wing area 12.0 m² (129.2 sq ft)
Wing section Wortmann FX-05-171/121
Aspect ratio 18.8
Empty weight 230 kg (507 lb)
Max weight 310 kg (683 lb)
Water ballast None
Max wing loading 25.83 kg/m² (5.29 lb/sq ft)
Max speed 138 kt (255 km/h)
Stalling speed 33 kt (61 km/h)
Min sinking speed at 42 kt (78 km/h) 0.66 m (2.2 ft)/sec
Max rough air speed 86 kt (160 km/h)
Best glide ratio at 51 kt (95 km/h) 36

Canada / **Marsden Gemini**

The Gemini is a high-performance side-by-side two-seat sailplane designed by Dr D. J. Marsden of Alberta University. It was conceived as a research project with the proviso that plans for home-building would be made available if enough interest in this variable-geometry sailplane was shown. To give a high coefficient of lift for climbing in thermals, Dr Marsden decided on mechanically simple slotted flaps rather than the camber-changing flaps used on some high-performance sailplanes.

The metal wings, made in four pieces of approximately equal weight, feature full-span slotted flaps. The outer flap sections also operate as ailerons and the inner 2.5 m (8 ft 3 in) sections deflect to 75° for landing control. These manually operated flaps are retracted for cruising and are extended to 10° down for thermalling.

The fuselage is of metal, the fore part being made of metal-framed glassfibre. The swept fin, with all-moving tailplane mounted on top, is faired to the aft fuselage. Landing gear consists of a manually retractable monowheel and a fixed tailwheel.

A 15 m version with a single seat is currently under construction. Flown by Dr Marsden, the Gemini now holds the Canadian 100km and 300km triangle speed records.

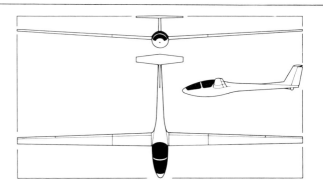

Data Gemini
Manufacturer E. Dumas, M.D. Jones and D.J. Marsden
First flight October 1973
Wing span 18.45 m (60 ft 6 in)
Length 7.77 m (25 ft 6 in)
Height 1.52 m (5 ft 0 in)
Wing area 11.5 m² (124 sq ft)
Wing section Wortmann FX-61-163 (slotted flap)
Aspect ratio 29.5
Empty weight 357 kg (785 lb)
Max weight 545 kg (1,200 lb)
Water ballast None
Max wing loading 47.4 kg/m² (9.7 lb/sq ft)
Stalling speed 35 kt (65 km/h)
Min sinking speed at 43 kt (80 km/h) 0.75 m (2.46 ft)/sec
Best glide ratio at 60 kt (110 km/h) 38

LET Blanik / Czechoslovakia

Since the first L-13 Blanik was rolled out in March 1956, thousands of glider pilots all over the world have received their training in this tandem-seat aircraft. By the summer of 1977 about 2,500 Blaniks had been built, of which more than 2,000 were for export. Production continues.

Designed by Karel Dlouhy, the Blanik has all-metal single-spar wings with an auxiliary rear spar carrying the hinges and tracks, and DFS airbrakes and Fowler type flaps. The semi-monocoque fuselage is constructed in two halves and riveted together in the vertical plane. The only non-metal parts are the fabric coverings on the control surfaces. The Blanik is fully stressed for aerobatics and this feature,

together with its sound construction, excellent flying qualities, durability and ease of servicing, have contributed to its popularity.

This aircraft has appeared no less than thirteen times in the FAI world record list as well as setting many national records. In 1969 the Chilean pilot Alijo Williamson was awarded the FAI Lilienthal medal for his 5 hr 51 min flight across the Andes in a Blanik.

In 1969 a small quantity was built of a powered version, the L-13J, using an Avia M150 Jawa 3-cylinder engine of 42 hp, but this version is not in series production.

Data L-13 Blanik
Manufacturer LET
First flight March 1956
Wing span 16.2 m (53 ft 1¾ in)
Length 8.4 m (27 ft 6¾ in)
Height 2.09 m (6 ft 10 in)
Wing area 19.15 m² (206.2 sq ft)
Wing section NACA 63₂ A615/612
Aspect ratio 13.7
Empty weight 292 kg (644 lb)
Max weight 500 kg (1,102 lb)
Water ballast None
Max wing loading 26.1 kg/m² (5.34 lb/sq ft)
Max speed 130 kt (240 km/h)
Stalling speed 32.4 kt (60 km/h)
Min sinking speed at 45 kt (83 km/h) 0.84 m (2.8 ft)/sec
Max rough air speed 78 kt (145 km/h)
Best glide ratio at 50 kt (93 km/h) 28.2

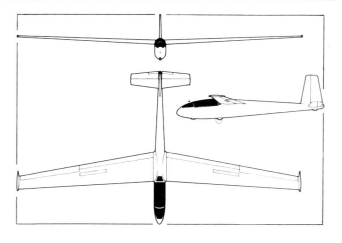

Czechoslovakia / **VSO 10**

The Czechoslovakian VSO 10 was the winner of the first International Club Class competition, held in Sweden in summer 1979. In a field of 33 the VSO 10C took first and second places, piloted by M. Brunecky and J. Vavra respectively. The VSO 10 was designed as a single-seat Standard Class sailplane but, to comply with Club Class rules, the retractable landing wheel was locked down and covered with a large glassfibre fairing. This version (photo) had the suffix C added to its designation.

Designed by Jan Janovec and his team in 1972 and embodying experience gained with the VSB 66S, the V-tail 15 m single-seater which flew in 1970, the VSO 10 has notably clean lines. Work on three prototypes began at Vyvojova Skupina Orlican, Chocen, in 1975 and the first flew on 26 October 1976.

The VSO 10 is of mixed construction, comprising a glassfibre cockpit shell and aluminium alloy rear fuselage, with a steel tube structure carrying the wings and undercarriage attachments. The metal T-tail has a fabric-covered elevator and rudder. The cantilever shoulder-set wing is a single-spar all-wood structure incorporating wooden slotted ailerons and metal DFS airbrakes on the upper surfaces.

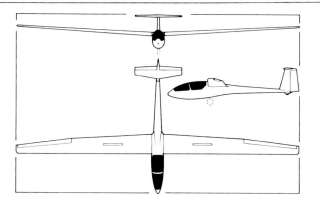

Data VSO 10
Manufacturer Vyvojova Skupina Orlican
First flight October 1976
Wing span 15.0 m (49 ft 2½ in)
Length 7.0 m (23 ft)
Height 1.20 m (3 ft 11¼ in)
Wing area 12.0 m² (129.167 sq ft)
Wing section Wortmann FX-61-163/FX-60-126
Aspect ratio 18.75
Empty weight 234.4 kg (516.76 lb)
Max weight 380 kg (837.76 lb)
Water ballast None
Max wing loading 31.67 kg/m² (6.49 lb/sq ft)
Max speed 140 kt (260 km/h)
Stalling speed 37 kt (68 km/h)
Min sinking speed at 39 kt (72 km/h) 0.63 m (2.07 ft)/sec
Max rough air speed 88 kt (163 km/h)
Best glide ratio at 51 kt (94 km/h) 36.2

The PIK-20 is the latest development in the long series of PIK sailplanes designed by Pekka Tammi. It started with a group of enthusiasts at the Helsinki Institute of Technology who in 1971 designed and built a glassfibre tug, inspiring others to investigate the possibilities of glassfibre sailplanes. The PIK-20 is a 15 m Unrestricted Class sailplane incorporating flaps with different settings for speed flying and thermalling. It first flew in October 1973.

In 1975 the manufacturers changed their name to Eiri Avion and were producing the PIK-20B (photo), which features interconnecting flaps and ailerons, 140 kg (309 lb) water ballast capacity, pneumatically sealed side-hinged canopy,

and optional carbon-fibre wing spars. The flaps move between ± 12° for normal flying and lower to 90° for full braking action and landing. The PIK-20B has won several national championships and took the first three places in the Standard Class at the 1976 World Championships in Finland. About 150 have been built.

The PIK-20D is the current production version, featuring carbon-fibre wing spars, a more pointed nose and upper-surface airbrakes. The flaps operate from −12° to + 16°. The rudder area was increased by moving the tailplane 12 cm (4.7 in) forward. The 20D first flew in 1976 and by the summer of 1979 some 200 had been built.

Data PIK-20D
Manufacturer Eiri Avion
First flight April 1976
Wing span 15.0 m (49 ft 2½ in)
Length 6.45 m (21 ft 2 in)
Height 1.45 m (4 ft 8 in)
Wing area 10.0 m² (107.7 sq ft)
Wing section Wortmann FX-67-K-170/150
Aspect ratio 22.5
Empty weight 220 kg (480 lb)
Max weight 450 kg (992 lb)
Water ballast 140 kg (309 lb)
Max wing loading 45kg/m² (9.21 lb/sq ft)
Max speed 158 kt (292 km/h)
Stalling speed 32 kt (60 km/h)
Min sinking speed at 39 kt (73 km/h) 0.56 m (1.84 ft)/sec
Max rough air speed 130 kt (240 km/h)
Best glide ratio at 63 kt (117 km/h) 42

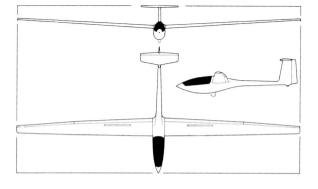

Finland / **Eiri PIK-20E**

The chief designer of Eiri Avion, Jukka Tervamäki, has adapted the PIK-20D to incorporate an engine. This aircraft is designated the PIK-20E and meets the OSTIV airworthiness regulations for powered sailplanes.

The power unit is a 31.6 kW (43 hp) Rotax 503 two-stroke piston engine which drives a two-blade wooden propeller. An electric starter is fitted. The engine is mounted on a pylon aft of the cockpit and is completely retractable by means of a handwheel situated on the starboard side of the cockpit. The carbon fibre-reinforced fuselage is similar to that of the 20D except for the cockpit, which has been lengthened by 80 mm to accommodate the 33 litre fuel tank behind the pilot's seat.

The original tailwheel has been replaced by a steerable wheel mounted on a steel sprung skid, and wingtip nylon wheels are fitted. The wing, swept back by 1° 36′, is fitted with large upper-surface airbrakes and the span of the tailplane has been increased by 0.4 m.

The prototype first flew in November 1976, powered by a 22.4 kW (30 hp) Kohler 440 cc engine. The production machine, with the Rotax engine, flew in March 1978 and went into production in the summer of that year.

Type   PIK-20E
Manufacturer   Eiri Avion
Country of origin   Finland
First flight   November 1976
Wing span   15.0 m (49 ft 2½ in)
Length   6.53 m (21 ft 5 in)
Wing area   10.0 m² (107.7 sq ft)
Wing section   Wortmann FX-67-K-170/150/17
Aspect ratio   22.5
Empty weight   290 kg (639 lb)
Max weight   470 kg (1,036 lb)
Water ballast   120 kg (265 lb)
Max wing loading   47.0 kg/m² (9.63 lb/sq ft)
Max speed   154 kt (285 km/h)
Stalling speed   36 kt (66 km/h)
Min sinking speed at 42 kt (77 km/h)   0.6 m (2 ft)/sec
Best glide ratio at 63 kt (117 km/h)   41
Power plant   Rotax 501, 37.3 kW (50 hp) 500 cc

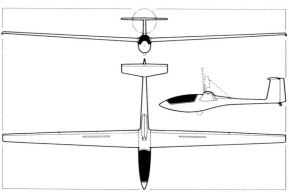

T-O run   450 m (1,476 ft)
Rate of climb   4.0 m (13 ft)/sec

Fibera KK-1 Utu / Finland

Designed by Dipl.-Eng. Ahto Anttila of Oy Fibera Ab, the prototype KK-1 Utu first flew on 14 August 1964. Since then four other prototypes, designated KK-1b, c, d, and e, have been built, each with various constructional techniques and structural modifications. The aim was to investigate the structural application of plastic laminates stabilised with polyurethane foam. As a result the superiority of plastic materials, especially when compared with wood, has become evident.

The wing consists of a glassfibre reinforced plastic (GRP) sandwich shell with a plastic foam core, a single I-spar and no ribs. The upper surface-hinged ailerons are of GRP shell construction with plastic foam stiffening. Trailing-edge flaps are fitted on both wings. The fuselage is a monocoque double-shell structure with glassfibre laminates. The tail fin is moulded integrally with the fuselage and the tailplane is mounted on the top of the fin. A non-retractable monowheel with drum brake is fitted.

A total of 22 examples had been built by early 1970, but the company is no longer in existence and only a few Utus are still flying.

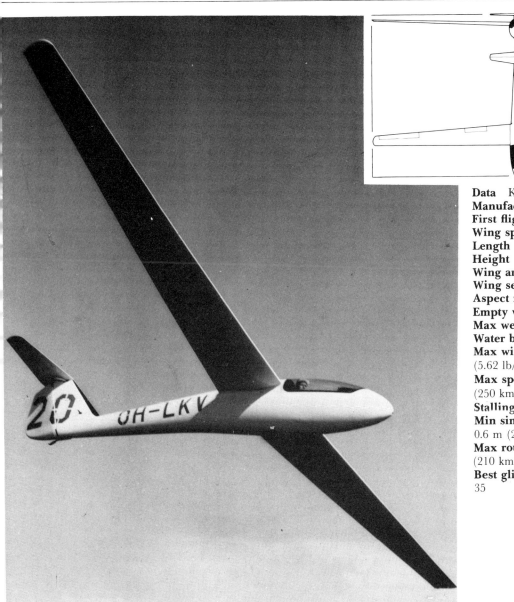

Data KK-1e Utu
Manufacturer Fibera
First flight 1964
Wing span 15.0 m (49 ft 2½ in)
Length 6.5 m (21 ft 4 in)
Height 1.22 m (4 ft 0 in)
Wing area 11.3 m² (121.6 sq ft)
Wing section NACA 63₃618/63612
Aspect ratio 20.0
Empty weight 200 kg (441 lb)
Max weight 310 kg (683 lb)
Water ballast None
Max wing loading 27.43 kg/m² (5.62 lb/sq ft)
Max speed (smooth air) 135 kt (250 km/h)
Stalling speed 34 kt (63 km/h)
Min sinking speed at 40 kt (74 km/h) 0.6 m (2 ft)/sec
Max rough air speed 113 kt (210 km/h)
Best glide ratio at 43.5 kt (81 km/h) 35

Finland / **IKV-3 Kotka**

Mr Tuomo Tervo, who supervised the construction of the PIK-3C, and Mr Jorma Jalkanen, who with Tervo was involved in the design and building of the PIK-16 Vasama and Havukka sailplanes, have together designed the single-seat high performance IKV-3. Construction of the prototype by members of IKV, the flying club of Vasama, was started in mid-1965, supervised by K.K. Lehtovaara Oy; the IKV-3 was later manufactured in series by Ilmailukerho.

The cantilever single-spar wooden wings are ply skinned and the ailerons and trailing-edge flaps are constructed from ply covered plastic foam. The airbrakes, of which there are two pairs on each wing, operate on both upper and lower surfaces and are constructed of light alloy. The fuselage is a conventional wooden structure with a long slender glassfibre nose and flush canopy. The ply tailplane is of the variable incidence type. The rudder and elevator are fabric covered. The landing gear consists of a retractable monowheel with drum brake and a detachable tail wheel.

On 28 May 1968 a Scandinavian record of 602 km (325 nm) was set up by S. Hämälänen in an IKV-3.

Data   IKV-3 Kotka
Manufacturer   IKV
First flight   June 1966
Wing span   18.2 m (59 ft 8½ in)
Length   7.75 m (25 ft 5 in)
Height   2.0 m (6 ft 6½ in)
Wing area   17.0 m² (183 sq ft)
Wing section   Wortmann FX-62-K153/FX-60-126
Aspect ratio   19.0
Empty weight   340 kg (750 lb)
Max weight   450 kg (992 lb)
Water ballast   None
Max wing loading   26.47 kg/m² (5.42 lb/sq ft)
Max speed   135 kt (250 km/h)
Stalling speed   28 kt (52 km/h)
Min sinking speed at 37.5 kt (70 km/h)   0.53 m (1.7 ft)/sec
Max rough air speed   93 kt (172 km/h)
Best glide ratio at 54 kt (100 km/h)   38

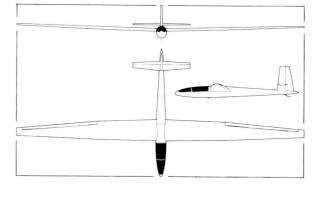

PIK-3C Kajava / Finland

The PIK series takes its name from the Polyteknikkojen Ilmailukerho, which was founded at Helsinki Technical University in 1931. The series began in 1945 but the PIK-3 was the first type to be produced in series. It was designed by Lars Norrmen and Ilkka Lounama as a small cheap sailplane suitable for construction by flying clubs. The prototype first flew in the summer of 1950.

The oval fuselage is of wood with diagonal ply covering. The conventional tail has a ply-covered fin and stabilisers. The detachable Plexiglas canopy runs back as far as the main spar. The high-set single-spar two-part wings are of wood and incorporate flaps and ailerons. Production PIK-3Bs, developed by Aush Koskinen, omitted the flaps and substituted airbrakes. Twenty PIK-3A and 3B models have been built.

The PIK-3C Kajava was a high performance version of the PIK-3B. The basic 13-metre wing was increased to 15 metre span and modifications were made to the Standard class rules. The wing structure was completely revised but the PIK-3B fuselage was retained but with a new canopy fitted. The prototype PIK-3C first flew on 20 May 1958 and the design was adopted for series production by S. Ilmailuliitto in the winter of 1958 under the supervision of Tuomo Tervo.

Data PIK-3C Kajava
Manufacturer Ilmailukerho
First flight May 1958
Wing span 15.0 m (49 ft 2½ in)
Length 6.6 m (21 ft 7¾ in)
Height 1.0 m (3 ft 3 in)
Wing area 13.1 m² (141 sq ft)
Wing section Göttingen 549/693
Aspect ratio 17.1
Empty weight 165 kg (364 lb)
Max weight 280 kg (617 lb)
Water ballast None
Max wing loading 21.4 kg/m² (4.38 lb/sq ft)
Max speed 135 kt (250 km/h)
Stalling speed 30 kt (55 km/h)
Min sinking speed at 35 kt (65 km/h) 0.61 m (2 ft)/sec
Max rough air speed 78 kt (145 km/h)
Best glide ratio at 40.5 kt (75 km/h) 30

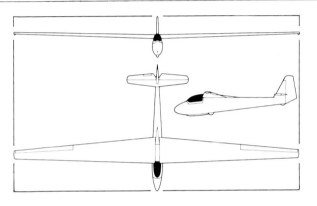

Finland / **PIK-16C Vasama**

In 1963 the OSTIV prize for the best Standard class sailplane was awarded to the Finnish designed and built PIK-16C Vasama. It was designed by Tuomo Tervo, Jorma Jalkanen and Kurt Hedström and was a development of the PIK-3A Kajava. It first flew in June 1961.

The single-seat PIK-16C has a conventional tail unit in place of the V-tail of the prototype, and the wings have been improved by using a sandwich type construction at the leading edge. The wing is built entirely of pine and birch wood and a striking feature of its design is its exceptional thinness, chosen to attain the optimum glide angle. The spoilers operate on top and bottom surfaces of the wing and the plain ailerons are of ply-covered wooden construction. The highly polished surface areas contribute to this sailplane's high performance. The monocoque fuselage is of wooden construction with a glassfibre nose. The landing gear comprises a non-retractable monowheel with brake, and a skid.

The PIK-16C was produced by K.K. Lehtovaara Oy, and a total of fifty-six PIK-16A, B and Cs was built. Several Finnish records were set with the Vasama and at the 1963 World championships in Argentina, Juhani Horma was placed third.

Data   PIK-16C Vasama
Manufacturer   K.K. Lehtovaara Oy
First flight   June 1961
Wing span   15.0 m (49 ft 2½ in)
Length   5.97 m (19 ft 7 in)
Height   1.45 m (4 ft 9 in)
Wing area   11.7 m² (126 sq ft)
Wing section   Wortmann FX-05-188/NACA 63_2615
Aspect ratio   19.2
Empty weight   190 kg (419 lb)
Max weight   300 kg (661 lb)
Water ballast   None
Max wing loading   25.64 kg/m² (5.25 lb/sq ft)
Max speed   135 kt (250 km/h)
Stalling speed   33.5 kt (62 km/h)
Min sinking speed at 39.5 kt (73 km/h)   0.59 m (1.9 ft)/sec
Max rough air speed   92 kt (170 km/h)
Best glide ratio at 46 kt (85 km/h)   34

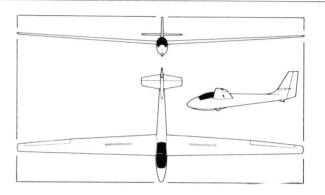

Breguet 901 /France

The first sailplane produced by the long established French aircraft firm of Breguet was the Breguet 900, which flew 470 km (254 nm) on its first flight in 1949. Four years later the Breguet 901 was developed and turned out to be one of France's most successful sailplanes.

The single-seat 901 designed by J. Cayla was ahead of its time, featuring multi-hinged Fowler flaps and ailerons. The large blown Plexiglas canopy is inset flush with the fuselage, setting a precedent for modern sailplanes, and 75 kg (165 lb) of water ballast are carried in the wings and can be discharged through openings on each side of the fuselage just beneath the wings.

Built entirely of wood, it has ply- and fabric-covered single-spar wings and tail unit and a wooden monocoque fuselage which is aerodynamically clean but has the disadvantage of a large hole left in the bottom when the wheel is retracted.

The Breguet 901-S1 is a modified version of the 901 with different flaps and a slightly longer fuselage and larger tailplane. It first flew in 1956, the same year that the tandem two-seat 20-metre Breguet 904 was produced. The 901 showed its worth by winning the World Championships twice, in 1954 and 1956.

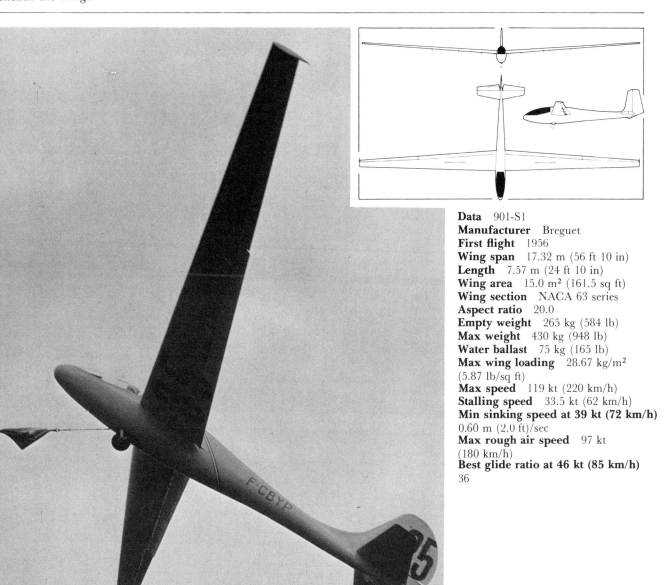

Data 901-S1
Manufacturer Breguet
First flight 1956
Wing span 17.32 m (56 ft 10 in)
Length 7.57 m (24 ft 10 in)
Wing area 15.0 m² (161.5 sq ft)
Wing section NACA 63 series
Aspect ratio 20.0
Empty weight 265 kg (584 lb)
Max weight 430 kg (948 lb)
Water ballast 75 kg (165 lb)
Max wing loading 28.67 kg/m² (5.87 lb/sq ft)
Max speed 119 kt (220 km/h)
Stalling speed 33.5 kt (62 km/h)
Min sinking speed at 39 kt (72 km/h) 0.60 m (2.0 ft)/sec
Max rough air speed 97 kt (180 km/h)
Best glide ratio at 46 kt (85 km/h) 36

France / **Breguet 905 Fauvette**

Of all the firms which have built sailplanes, Breguet is one of the best known outside France because of the success of its designs. The Breguet 905 Fauvette is a single-seat Standard Class V-tail sailplane designed by J Cayla. At the time of its manufacture it was available either complete or as a kit of parts for home assembly.

The fuselage consists of three main parts: a nose section of moulded plastic foam housing the pilot's seat, instrument panel and flying controls; a steel-tube centre fuselage covered with a moulded polystyrene skin which carries cockpit attachment points, towing hook and wing; and a rear fuselage of plywood/foam sandwich construction. The

sandwich is composed of 6 mm plywood with 8 mm of Klégécel, an expanded plastic. The Klégécel is pre-formed under heat and the result is an almost perfect shape of considerable strength and lightness. The sandwich is also used for the fixed tail surfaces which fold to the vertical position for trailering. The cantilever single-spar wings are of ply and Klégécel with metal and Klégécel sandwich airbrakes.

On 12 June 1959 Rear Admiral N. Goodhart set a United Kingdom distance record in a Fauvette by flying a distance of 625 km (337 nm).

Data   905 Fauvette
Manufacturer   Breguet
First flight   1958
Wing span   15.0 m (49 ft 2½ in)
Length   6.22 m (20 ft 4¾ in)
Wing area   11.25 m² (121.1 sq ft)
Wing section   NACA 63420/63613
Aspect ratio   20.0
Empty weight   155 kg (342 lb)
Max weight   275 kg (606 lb)
Water ballast   None
Max wing loading   24.5 kg/m² (5.02 lb/sq ft)
Max speed   108 kt (200 km/h)
Stalling speed   29 kt (54 km/h)
Min sinking speed at 35 kt (65 km/h)   0.65 m (2.1 ft)/sec
Max rough air speed   92 kt (170 km/h)
Best glide ratio at 42 kt (78 km/h)   30

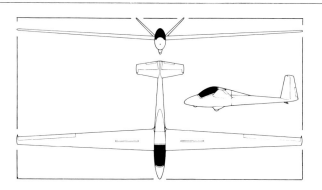

CARMAM JP.15-36 Aiglon / France

The JP.15-36 is a restricted Standard Class sailplane designed by Robert Jaquet and Jean Pottier, Technical Directors of CARMAM, as a private venture. It is built by CARMAM, who have been building the M-100 and M-200 under licence for Morelli of Italy and have manufactured sailplane components for Glasflügel of W. Germany. The prototype JP.15-36 made its first flight on 14 June 1974. The sailplane is of all glassfibre/Klégécel sandwich construction, with an all-flying tail of conventional configuration and a fixed landing wheel and cable brake. It was designed for intensive use by clubs and so has good flying qualities and safe away-landing characteristics for inexperienced pilots. The cockpit, under a one-piece blown canopy, is large and comfortable. Both the seat and rudder pedals are adjustable in flight. The wings, fitted with Schempp-Hirth type airbrakes, are designed to allow fast and easy rigging with the aileron and airbrake controls connected automatically.

The PA.15-35 is a version designed by Jean Pottier to be suitable for amateur builders. The JP.15-36AR is a version with retractable monowheel and capacity for 80 litres of water ballast.

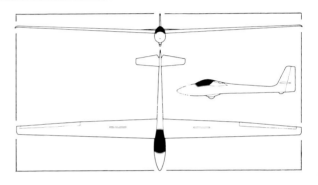

Data JP.15-36 Aiglon
Manufacturer CARMAM
First flight June 1974
Wing span 15.0 m (49 ft 2½ in)
Length 6.4 m (21 ft 0 in)
Height 1.4 m (4 ft 7 in)
Wing area 11.0 m² (118.4 sq ft)
Wing section Wortmann FX-67-K-170/67-126
Aspect ratio 20.4
Empty weight 200 kg (441 lb)
Max weight 390 kg (860 lb)
Water ballast None
Max wing loading 35.5 kg/m² (7.27 lb/sq ft)
Max speed 130 kt (240 km/h)
Stalling speed 33.5 kt (62 km/h)
Min sinking speed at 40.5 kt (75 km/h) 0.6 m (2 ft)/sec
Max rough air speed 108 kt (200 km/h)
Best glide ratio at 49.5 kt (92 km/h) 36

France / **Fauvel AV.45**

The AV.45 is a single-seat tailless motor glider which first flew on 4 May 1960 powered by a 26 kW (35 hp) Nelson engine. A second prototype with a 16.5 kW (22 hp) SOLO engine was built by Société Aéronautique Normande (SAN). The standard engine recommended for the AV.45, however, is the modified Hirth 0-280R of between 30-41 kW (40-55 hp).

The single-spar wooden wing has conventional ailerons and also elevators on the trailing edge of the centre wing. Schempp-Hirth airbrakes are mounted both on upper and lower surfaces of the outer wings. The fuselage consists of a short wooden nacelle with glassfibre covering. The twin fin

and rudders are inset at the junctions of the centre section and outer wings. As with the AV.361, the AV.45 may also be fitted with a Wortmann laminar-flow wing which increase the best glide angle to 30 at a speed of 47.5 kt (88 km/h). An improved version of the AV.45, known as the AV.45 has been built. Modifications include a wing of extended span; a more tapered nose; more streamlined wheel fairings and vertical tail surfaces of Wortmann symmetrical section.

Data AV.45
Manufacturer Fauvel
First flight May 1960
Wing span 13.74 m (45 ft 1 in)
Length 3.59 m (11 ft 9 in)
Wing area 15.95 m² (171.7 sq ft)
Wing section F2 17%
Aspect ratio 11.84
Empty weight 216 kg (476 lb)
Max weight 350 kg (772 lb)
Water ballast None
Max wing loading 21.94 kg/m² (4.49 lb/sq ft)
Max speed 77 kt (142 km/h)
Min sinking speed at 37.5 kt (70 km/h) 0.8 m (2.62 ft)/sec
Best glide ratio at 45.5 kt (85 km/h) 27
Power plant Hirth O-280R, 30-41 kW (40-55 hp)
T-O run 493 ft (150 m)
Rate of climb 168 m (550 ft)/min

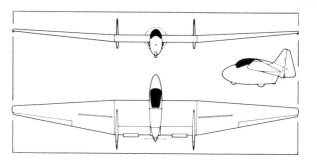

The AV.222 side-by-side two-seat tailless motor glider is a lighter and simplified version of the AV.221; both are derived from the AV.22 tailless sailplane. The AV.222 is suitable for amateur construction and plans are available from Fauvel. Glassfibre component moulds and canopies can also be supplied if required.

The AV.221 and 222 can be powered by a 30 kW (39 hp) Rectimo 4AR 1200 or 45 kW (60 hp) Limbach Volkswagen conversion, driving a fixed pitch wooden propeller of 1.05 m (3 ft 5¼ in) diameter. The prototype AV.221 flew for the first time in April 1965. To improve ease of handling over rough terrain the original large single landing wheel has been replaced by a conventional layout of twin wheels on cantilever legs of laminated glassfibre, fitted with disc brakes. There is no increase in drag from these faired wheels, and the outrigger wheels of the prototype have been removed.

The wings, of wooden construction, are swept slightly forward. They are made in three sections with the centre section being mounted on the short fuselage and the outer panels attached to the centre section. The fuselage incorporates a large single fin and rudder and is fitted with a steerable tail wheel.

Data AV.222
Manufacturer Fauvel
First flight April 1965
Wing span 16.4 m (53 ft 9¾ in)
Length 5.22 m (17 ft 1½ in)
Wing area 23.0 m² (247.6 sq ft)
Wing section F₂ 17%
Aspect ratio 12.0
Empty weight 325 kg (716 lb)
Max weight 550 kg (1,212 lb)
Water ballast None
Max wing loading 23.91 kg/m² (4.89 lb/sq ft)
Stalling speed 40 kt (74 km/h)
Min sinking speed at 40 kt (74 km/h) 0.87 m (2.85 ft)/sec
Best glide ratio at 46 kt (85 km/h) 26
Power plant Limbach, 45 kW (60 hp)
T-O run 110 m (361 ft)
Max rate of climb at S/L 180 m (591 ft)/min

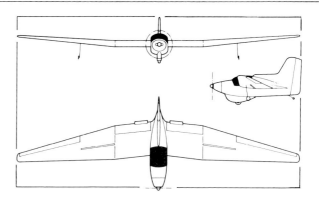

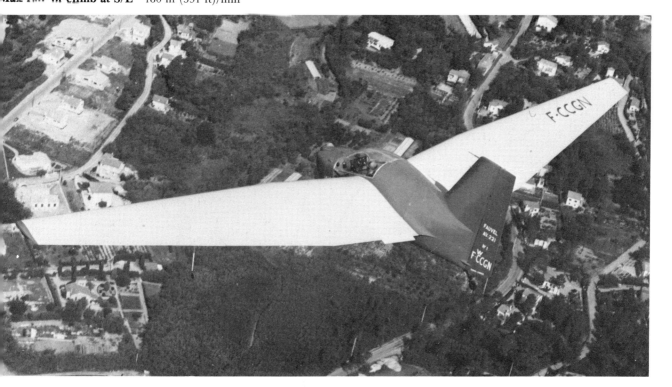

France / **Fauvel AV.361**

Flying wing sailplanes have excited wide interest for many years with their obvious advantages of low drag and simplicity of design and construction. However, they have been beset with problems, chiefly connected with questions of stability, which has forced most designers to concentrate on the highly swept back design with high aspect ratio. The AV.36 Monobloc, designed and built by Charles Fauvel, has proved that the problem of stability did not really exist in practice. This sailplane was supplied in kit form in the early 1950s and more than 100 were sold to customers in 14 countries before the design was superseded by the AV.361.

In the AV.361, which first flew in 1960, the span of the wood and fabric wings has been increased from 11.95 m (39 ft 2½ in) to 12.78 m (41 ft 11¼ in). Schempp-Hirth spoilers are fitted on both upper and lower wing surfaces. The new fin and rudder design on the AV.361, together with the larger ailerons, have improved control co-ordination. The fuselage consists of a short wooden nacelle and the roomy cockpit is covered by a side-opening blown Plexiglas canopy. A nose wheel and rear skid have replaced the long skid of the AV.36. Although commercial production of this aircraft ceased in 1971, plans for home constructors are still available.

Data AV.361
Manufacturer Fauvel
First flight 1960
Wing span 12.78 m (41 ft 11¼ in)
Length 3.24 m (10 ft 7½ in)
Wing area 14.6 m² (157.2 sq ft)
Wing section F₂ 17%
Aspect ratio 11.4
Empty weight 122 kg (269 lb)
Max weight 258 kg (569 lb)
Water ballast None
Max wing loading 17.67 kg/m² (3.62 lb/sq ft)
Max speed 119 kt (220 km/h)
Stalling speed 31 kt (58 km/h)
Min sinking speed at 35 kt (65 km/h) 0.75 m (2.5 ft)/sec
Max rough air speed 85 kt (158 km/h)
Best glide ratio at 45 kt (83 km/h) 26

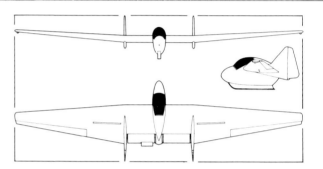

Fournier RF-9 / France

Avions Fournier is a company which in the past has built light aircraft rather than motor gliders. In the mid 1960s they produced the RF-4D, constructed of wood with glassfibre fairings, and the RF-5. Sportavia, who build the Fourniers in West Germany, collaborated with Scheibe to produce the SFS-31 Milan, which is an RF-4 with a feathering propeller and the 15-metre wing of the Scheibe SF-27. The SF-27M motor glider, built by Scheibe, differs from the SFS-31 Milan in that the latter has the power unit and propeller sited in the nose cone. The RF-4, RF-5 and Milan are all lower performance motor gliders.

In France, Avions Fournier designed and built the single-seat RF-7 with wood fuselage and single-spar wooden wings covered with plywood and fabric of 9.4 m (30 ft 10 in) span. It is powered by a 65 hp Sportavia Limbach SL 1700D engine.

The latest Fournier product is designated the RF-9. It is a two-seat motor glider intended for training. The accommodation is arranged side-by-side. It is powered by a 50 kW (68 hp) Limbach SL 1700E engine driving a Hoffmann two-blade variable-pitch propeller. Fuel capacity is 30 litres (6.6. Imp Gal). First flight was on 20 January 1977.

Data RF-9
Manufacturer Fournier
First flight January 1977
Wing span 17.0 m (55 ft 9¼ in)
Length 7.86 m (25 ft 9½ in)
Wing area 18.0 m² (193.8 sq ft)
Wing section NACA 64₃618
Aspect ratio 16.0
Empty weight 530 kg (1,168 lb)
Max weight 750 kg (1,653 lb)
Water ballast None
Max wing loading 38.8 kg/m² (7.59 lb/sq ft)
Max level speed at S/L 102 kt (190 km/h)
Stalling speed 35.5 kt (65 km/h)
Min sinking speed at 43.5 kt (80 km/h) 0.80 m (2.6 ft)/sec
Best glide ratio 28
Power plant Sportavia Limbach SL 1700E, 50 kW (68 hp)
T-O run 100 m (328 ft)

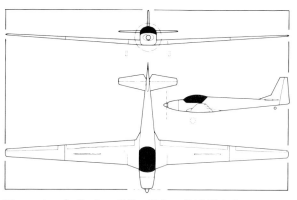

Max rate of climb at S/L 156 m (512 ft)/min
Range 600 km (324 nm)

France / **GEP TCV-03 Trucavaysse**

The TCV-03 is a single-seat Standard Class sailplane, built by GEP (Groupe d'Études Georges Payre) in an attempt to produce a sailplane which has good flying characteristics and which can be sold in kit form suitable for amateur or club construction. Prototype construction started in February 1969 and the aircraft first flew on 14 July 1973.

The design is based on the original Breguet 905, with modifications. These include an improved control system, reinforced trailing edges, a new slender fuselage and the deletion of the landing skid. It was designed by Dr P. Vaysse, head of the sailplane amateur construction department of the FFVV (Fédération Française de Vol à Voile) and is his third project. The first two were the TCV-01 and the TCV-02, which flew for the first time in August 1964 and April 1969 respectively.

The TCV-03 features single-spar cantilever shoulder wings with plywood/Klégécel sandwich leading edges, slotted wooden ailerons and DFS metal airbrakes on both upper and lower surfaces. The fuselage is a conventional ply-covered wooden structure, and the tail unit features an all-moving tailplane. The landing gear consists of a fixed monowheel and tail skid, employing rubber shock absorbers.

Data TCV-03 Trucavaysse
Manufacturer Group d'Etudes Georges Payre (GEP)
First flight July 1973
Wing span 15.0 m (49 ft 2½ in)
Length 6.7 m (21 ft 11¾ in)
Height 1.8 m (5 ft 11 in)
Wing area 11.25 m² (121.1 sq ft)
Wing section NACA 63-420/513
Aspect ratio 20.0
Empty weight 192 kg (423 lb)
Max weight 302 kg (666 lb)
Water ballast None
Max wing loading 26.9 kg/m² (5.51 lb/sq ft)
Max speed 113 kt (210 km/h)
Stalling speed 27 kt (50 km/h)
Min sinking speed at 32.5 kt (60 km/h) 0.8 m (2.6 ft)/sec
Max rough air speed 81 kt (150 km/h)
Best glide ratio at 43 kt (80 km/h) 28

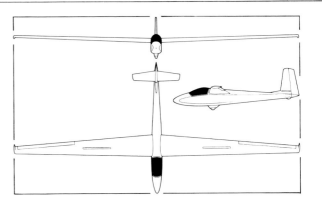

Issoire D 77 Iris / France

Siren SA, which designed the Edelweiss sailplanes and the two-seat E 78 Silène, began designing the D 77 Iris in 1973 as a single-seat training sailplane. It made its debut in 1977 and after its first flight on 26 February was exhibited at the Paris Air Show. In the same year Issoire Aviation was formed by Siren SA to produce both the E 78 Silène and D 77 Iris. The D 77 is a cantilever mid-wing sailplane using a Bertin E55-166 wing section. It is of glassfibre/plastic foam sandwich construction and incorporates airbrakes on the upper surface of each wing. The original design projected a cantilever T-tail but the production model has a conventional tail unit with tailplane of fixed incidence and trim tabs on both sides of the elevator. The fuselage consists of a GRP monocoque structure, built in two halves and reinforced at the wing attachment points. A non-retractable monowheel with Siren hydraulic brakes and tail skid comprise the landing gear.

The cockpit contains a console for the instruments and an adjustable semi-reclining seat under a long clear one-piece flush canopy which opens sideways to starboard.

The D 77 is available as either a finished aircraft or a kit which requires only 400 man-hours to assemble.

Data D 77 Iris
Manufacturer Issoire
First flight February 1977
Wing span 13.5 m (44 ft 3½ in)
Length 6.37 m (20 ft 11 in)
Height 0.9 m (2 ft 11½ in)
Wing area 11.4 m² (122.7 sq ft)
Wing section Bertin E-55-166
Aspect ratio 16
Empty weight 220 kg (485 lb)
Max weight 330 kg (728 lb)
Water ballast None
Max wing loading 27.2 kg/m² (5.57 lb/sq ft)
Max speed 126 kt (234 km/h)
Stalling speed 32.5 kt (60 km/h)
Min sinking speed at 39.5 kt (73 km/h) 0.68 m (2.23 ft)/sec
Best glide ratio at 48.5 (90 km/h) 33

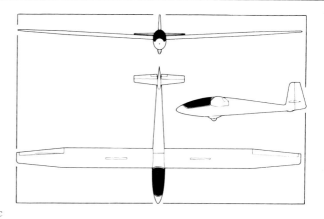

France / **Issoire E 78 Silène**

The E 78 Silène side-by-side two-seat sailplane was developed by CERVA (Consortium Européen de Réalisation et de Ventes d'Avions) and is the first French glassfibre two-seater. The company was owned by Siren SA and Wassmer-Aviation SA. The E 78 was designed by Siren and, following the closure of Wassmer, was transferred to Issoire in late 1977. The aim was to produce a sailplane suitable for all stages of glider training from ab initio to cross-country flights. Construction was started in February 1973 and the prototype first flew at Argenton on 2 July 1974. The wings are of glassfibre/plastic foam sandwich construction, incorporating two-section ailerons of similar material and Schempp-Hirth airbrakes operating both above and below each wing. Flaps are not fitted. The fuselage is a semi-monocoque glassfibre/plastic foam sandwich structure. The conventional tail unit incorporates a fixed incidence tailplane and trim tabs on each elevator. The pilots sit in staggered position to keep the width of the fuselage to a minimum, the starboard seat being set slightly to the rear. The Silène is available with either retractable or fixed landing wheel with hydraulic brake and shock absorber.

Data   E 78 Silène
Manufacturer   Issoire Aviation
First flight   July 1974
Wing span   18.0 m (59 ft 0¾ in)
Length   7.95 m (26 ft 1 in)
Height   1.5 m (4 ft 11 in)
Wing area   18.0 m² (193.8 sq ft)
Wing section   Bertin E55 166
Aspect ratio   18.0
Empty weight   365 kg (805 lb)
Max weight   565 kg (1,246 lb)
Water ballast   None
Max wing loading   29 kg/m² (5.94 lb/sq ft)
Max speed   119 kt (220 km/h)
Stalling speed   34 kt (63 km/h)
Min sinking speed at 39 kt (73 km/h)   0.59 m (1.8 ft)/sec
Best glide ratio at 51 kt (95 km/h)   38

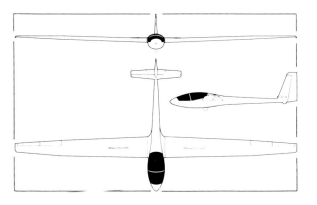

Siren Edelweiss / France

The Edelweiss, an elegant high performance single-seat Standard Class sailplane of the early 1960s, was designed by Dr J. Cayla and built by Siren SA. The prototype C.30S Edelweiss had swept-forward wings and a V-tail and was constructed mainly of plywood/Klégécel sandwich. In the production version the swept-forward wings were replaced and the ailerons, airbrakes and nose were shortened.

The shoulder-set cantilever wings consist of a single-spar foam-filled wooden structure incorporating only eight ribs, covered with a ply/Klégécel sandwich. The unslotted ailerons are metal and the airbrakes, which operate on both upper and lower wing surfaces, are interconnected with the hydraulic wheel brake. An interesting feature is the 50 kg (110 lb) ballast in the form of eight lead bars mounted in the wing roots so that the wing loading can be varied. The fuselage is constructed from a plywood/Klégécel sandwich with laminated nose and tail cones. The pilot sits in a semi-reclining position beneath a long slender canopy to which the instrument panel is attached.

The first of the two prototypes flew on 25 September 1962 and both competed in the 1963 World Championships in Argentina, gaining second and seventeenth places in the Standard Class. The prototype of an Open Class version, the 17.5 m Edelweiss 4, first flew on 9 May 1968.

Data C.30S Edelweiss
Manufacturer Siren
First flight September 1962
Wing span 15.0 m (49 ft 2½ in)
Length 7.5 m (24 ft 7 in)
Wing area 12.5 m² (134.5 sq ft)
Wing section NACA 64 series
Aspect ratio 18.0
Empty weight 235 kg (518 lb)
Max weight 380 kg (838 lb)
Water ballast None
Max wing loading 30.4 kg/m² (6.23 lb/sq ft)
Max speed 121 kt (220 km/h)
Stalling speed 35 kt (65 km/h)
Min sinking speed at 43 kt (80 km/h) 0.65 m (2.1 ft)/sec
Max rough air speed 86 kt (160 km/h)
Best glide ratio at 51 kt (95 km/h) 36

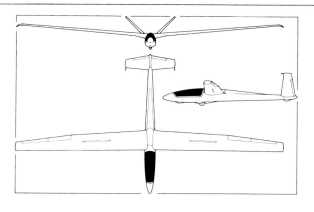

France / **Wassmer WA 22 Super Javelot**

The Wassmer light aircraft firm, based at Issoire in Central France, also built many of France's sailplanes. The company's first essay into the market was the 16.08 m WA 20 Javelot, designed by M. Colland and built to meet an urgent need for a single-seat sailplane with good performance and straightforward construction. The first flight of the WA 20 was made in August 1956.

The WA 22 Super Javelot is the Standard Class development of the WA 20 and is used in great numbers by French gliding clubs and private owners. The fuselage is a fabric-covered steel tube frame to which is bolted a glassfibre cockpit shell in three parts. The cockpit, under a new blown canopy, incorporates a seat which can be adjusted both for height and inclination. The three-piece wing is a single-spar wooden structure with outer panels set at an angle. Quick, easy rigging is effected by pulling on a large lever, which locks the securing bolts in position. The differential wooden ailerons are in two sections, the inner section moving through a larger angle than the outer section to improve the rate of roll. Perforated wooden airbrakes operate above and below each wing and the hydraulic wheelbrake is coupled with the airbrake control lever.

Data WA 22 Super Javelot
Manufacturer Wassmer
First flight June 1961
Wing span 15.0 m (49 ft 2½ in)
Length 7.06 m (23 ft 2 in)
Height 1.9 m (6 ft 3 in)
Wing area 14.4 m² (155 sq ft)
Wing section NACA 63821/63615
Aspect ratio 15.7
Empty weight 205 kg (452 lb)
Max weight 350 kg (750 lb)
Water ballast None
Max wing loading 24.3 kg/m² (4.84 lb/sq ft)
Max speed 108 kt (200 km/h)
Stalling speed 33 kt (61 km/h)
Min sinking speed at 43 kt (80 km/h) 0.7 m (2.29 ft)/sec
Max rough air speed 70 kt (130 km/h)
Best glide ratio 30

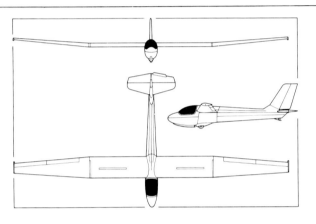

Wassmer WA 28 Espadon / France

The WA 28 Espadon (Swordfish) is the glassfibre version of the WA 26 Squale, which was a conventional wood and fabric sailplane. The wings of the WA 26 and WA 28 are identical in geometry, but the latter's are constructed from a glassfibre/plastic foam sandwich. The Schempp-Hirth airbrakes, operating both above and below the wings, are perforated and are claimed to be very effective.

The reinforced polyester plastic fuselage is of oval section, accommodating the pilot in a semi-reclining position beneath a long slender one-piece Plexiglas canopy which opens sideways to port. The tail unit is of conventional shape with all-moving horizontal surfaces and spring-loaded trimming. The seat, headrest and rudder pedals are all adjustable and ventilation is provided by swivel inlets. The instrument panel is large, housing a comprehensive set of equipment. The landing gear consists of a retractable wheel mounted forward of the centre of gravity, with hydraulic brake and an optional fixed tail wheel.

Design began in 1972 and the prototype WA 28 first flew in May 1974, with the first production model flying in November of that year.

Data WA 28 Espadon (Swordfish)
Manufacturer Wassmer
First flight 1974
Wing span 15.0 m (49 ft 2½ in)
Length 7.65 m (25 ft 1¼ in)
Height 1.66 m (5 ft 5½ in)
Wing area 12.63 m² (136 sq ft)
Wing section Wortmann FX-61-163/60-126
Aspect ratio 17.82
Empty weight 245 kg (540 lb)
Max weight 378 kg (833 lb)
Water ballast None
Max wing loading 29.92 kg/m² (6.13 lb/sq ft)
Max speed 131 kt (242 km/h)
Stalling speed 36.5 kt (68 km/h)
Max rough air speed 84.5 kt (157 km/h)
Best glide ratio at 48.5 kt (90 km/h) 38

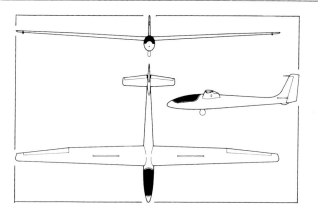

France / **Wassmer WA 30 Bijave**

The Wassmer WA 30 Bijave is the standard French two-seat advanced trainer and is a development of the WA 21 Javelot. Designed by M Colland, the first prototype flew on 17 December 1958. The second, improved prototype first flew on 18 March 1970, Although the type is no longer in production many are still flying, mainly in France.

The pilots sit in tandem with the rear seat placed somewhat higher than the front, providing very good visibility from the rear. Each seat has an individual blown perspex canopy. The shoulder-set cantilever wings, which are in three pieces, are constructed from birch plywood reinforced with a leading edge torsion box spar and with fabric covering aft of the spar.

The Schempp-Hirth airbrakes are perforated and operate on both upper and lower surfaces of the wings. The fuselage consists of a welded steel-tube frame covered with fabric; the nose cone is glassfibre. The landing gear consists of a retractable sprung monowheel and a large skid at the nose. The wooden all-moving tailplane is a one-piece cantilever structure with large anti-balance tabs.

Data WA 30 Bijave
Manufacturer Wassmer
First flight December 1958
Wing span 16.85 m (55 ft 3½ in)
Length 9.5 m (31 ft 2 in)
Height 2.74 m (9 ft 0 in)
Wing area 19.2 m² (206.7 sq ft)
Wing section NACA 63821/63615
Aspect ratio 15.0
Empty weight 295 kg (650 lb)
Max weight 550 kg (1,213 lb)
Water ballast None
Max wing loading 28.6 kg/m² (5.85 lb/sq ft)
Max speed 130 kt (240 km/h)
Stalling speed 32.5 kt (60 km/h)
Min sinking speed at 42 kt (78 km/h) 0.75 m (2.5 ft)/sec
Max rough air speed 81 kt (150 km/h)
Best glide ratio at 40.5 kt (75 km/h) 30

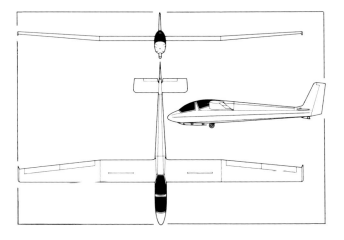

Akaflieg Braunschweig SB-9 Stratus / West Germany

At the 1969 German Nationals the Brunswick Flying College (Akaflieg Braunschweig), who have built a number of high performance sailplanes, introduced a new single-seat sailplane, the SB-9 Stratus. Calculations had suggested that a wing span of 22 metres and an aspect ratio of 31.3 would provide the performance they required. The SB-9 was developed from the 18 metre SB-8 and first flew on 23 January 1969. The glide ratio of the 22 m version is 48 compared with 42 for the SB-8 and the minimum sink speed is likewise improved from 0.52 m/sec to 0.45 m/sec. This represents a 15% gain in performance, but some difficulties had to be overcome: the wing geometry, load distribution, aileron length and rudder action posed problems and the maximum speed is limited to only 180 km/h (97 kt). Glassfibre with balsa wood support is used for the fuselage and PVC foam for the wing, which has a glassfibre roving spar to bear the stresses. The trailing-edge flaps are of the HKS type and are of elastic glassfibre construction with no hinge or gap. The tail unit is a glassfibre and balsa structure with the tailplane mounted at the tip of the fin. The landing gear consists of an unsprung retractable monowheel with drum brake. Later the wing span was reduced to 21 m (68 ft 11 in), improving the SB-9's maximum speed by 20 km/h (11 kt).

Data SB-9 Stratus
Manufacturer Akaflieg Braunschweig
First flight January 1969
Wing span 22.0 m (72 ft 2¼ in)
Length 7.5 m (24 ft 7¼ in)
Height 1.4 m (4 ft 7 in)
Wing area 15.48 m² (166.6 sq ft)
Wing section Wortmann
FX-62-K-153/131
Aspect ratio 31.3
Empty weight 314 kg (692 lb)
Max weight 416 kg (917 lb)
Water ballast None
Max wing loading 27.0 kg/m²
(5.53 lb/sq ft)
Max speed 97 kt (180 km/h)
Stalling speed 32 kt (59 km/h)
Min sinking speed at 39 kt (72 km/h)
0.45 m (1.5 ft)/sec
Max rough air speed 97 kt
(180 km/h)
Best glide ratio at 46 kt (85 km/h)
48

West Germany / **Akaflieg Braunschweig SB-10 Schirokko**

The Brunswick Technical University, having developed a long series of interesting experimental sailplanes, began design of this unique tandem two-seat high performance sailplane in 1969. It first flew on 22 July 1972.

The SB-10 has an aspect ratio of 36 and can be flown with a wing of either 26 m or 29 m span. It is developed from the single-seat SB-9 and uses the same outer wing panels with airbrakes but the centre section, fuselage and tail unit are new designs. The wings are in five parts: the centre section, constructed of plywood, balsa wood and carbon-fibre, gives rigidity, and the outer panels and wing tips are of balsa wood and glassfibre with foam filling. The camber-changing flaps are built of foam-filled carbon-fibre and can be drooped with the ailerons (there are three on the 29 metre version).

The fuselage is a steel tube frame covered with a shell of balsa/glassfibre sandwich and light alloy at the rear. The tail unit is a sweptback structure of balsa/glassfibre sandwich with a fixed incidence tailplane. The landing gear includes an air-assisted retractable monowheel with hydraulic brake and tail skid.

After some modifications, including changes to the rudder system, landing gear and airbrakes, the aircraft set a German distance record of 896 km (577 ml) on 16 April 1974.

Data SB-10
Manufacturer Akaflieg Braunschweig
First flight July 1972
Wing span 29.0 m (95 ft 1¾ in)
Length 10.36 m (33 ft 11¾ in)
Wing area 22.95 m² (247.1 sq ft)
Wing section Wortmann FX-62-K-153/131/60-126
Aspect ratio 36.6
Empty weight 577 kg (1,272 lb)
Max weight 897 kg (1,978 lb)
Water ballast 100 kg (220 lb)
Max wing loading 39 kg/m² (7.98 lb/sq ft)
Max speed 108 kt (200 km/h)
Stalling speed 35 kt (65 km/h)
Min sinking speed at 40.5 kt (75 km/h) 0.41 (1.3 ft)/sec
Max rough air speed 108 kt (200 km/h)
Best glide ratio at 48.5 kt (90 km/h) 53

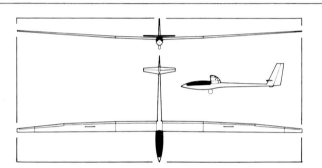

Akaflieg Braunschweig SB-11 / West Germany

Continuing its tradition of producing sailplanes featuring innovations of interest to both pilots and manufacturers, the Technical University of Brunswick has produced a single-seat 15 m Class sailplane. The SB-11, built almost entirely of carbon-reinforced glassfibre, has full-span Fowler flaps which can extend the wing area by up to 25 per cent. The shoulder-set wings, incorporating a specially developed Wortmann section, have carbon-fibre box-section spars with skins of carbon fibre and plastic foam sandwich. Camber-changing flaps and ailerons are hinged to the slotless Fowler flaps. All are manually operated. The gap between wing and flap has been sealed by making the Fowler flap thicker at its leading and trailing edges so that, when fully in or out, it fits snugly into its shrouds. There are Schempp-Hirth airbrakes on the upper surfaces of the wings. The fuselage is a carbon-fibre monocoque structure, the front of which was cast in Schleicher AS-W 20 moulds. The T-tailed rear fuselage is made on Schempp-Hirth Janus moulds.

The SB-11 made its first international appearance in the World Championships in Chateauroux, France, in 1978. Flown to victory by Helmut Reichmann, it showed a remarkable ability to make use of weak thermals.

Data SB-11
Manufacturer Akaflieg Braunschweig
First flight May 1978
Wing span 15.0 m (49 ft 2½ in)
Length 7.4 m (24 ft 3 in)
Height 1.47 m (4 ft 10 in)
Wing area 10.56 m² (113.7 sq ft)
Wing section Wortmann FX-62K-144/21-VG-1.25
Aspect ratio 21.3
Empty weight 270 kg (595 lb)
Max weight 470 kg (1,036 lb)
Water ballast 100 kg (220 lb)
Max wing loading 44.5 kg/m² (9.11 lb/sq ft)
Max speed 140 kt (260 km/h)
Stalling speed 31.5 kt (58 km/h)
Min sinking speed at 43 kt (80 km/h) 0.62 m (2.03 ft)/sec
Max rough air speed 97 kt (180 km/h)
Best glide ratio at 56 kt (104 km/h) 41

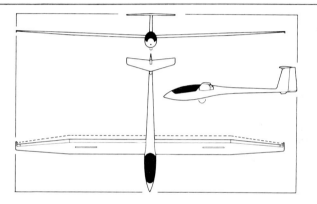

West Germany / **Akaflieg Darmstadt D-36 Circe**

Akaflieg Darmstadt's involvement with gliding started in 1909. Its successes include the Edith in 1922; the Konsul, the first 18 metre glider; the Darmstadt; the feather-weight Windspiel; the metal D-30 Cirrus; and after the war the D-34.

As far back as 1954 members of the Akaflieg Darmstadt began to investigate the possibilities of using the new synthetic materials which were becoming available, and in 1961 they were experimenting with reinforced glassfibre bonded resins. Three members of the DFS, Wolfe Lemke, Gerhard Waibel and Klaus Holighaus, started work on the D-36 Circe in the Spring of 1963.

The D-36 features a streamlined fuselage with a fixed front-section canopy with detachable rear section. A large retractable landing wheel is fitted. The T-tail set a precedent for many glassfibre sailplanes. The wings incorporate Schempp-Hirth airbrakes and camber-changing flaps which operate between ±10°. The material used is a balsa/glassfibre composite in the form of a sandwich.

The D-36 was rolled out at Gelnhausen for its first flight in March 1964. This new design was successful in gaining second place in the World Championships at South Cerney in 1965 and aroused keen interest.

Data D-36 Circe
Manufacturer Akaflieg Darmstadt
First flight March 1964
Wing span 17.8 m (58 ft 3½ in)
Length 7.35 m (24 ft 1½ in)
Wing area 12.8 m² (137.8 sq ft)
Wing section Wortmann FX-62-K-131/60-126
Aspect ratio 24.0
Empty weight 282 kg (622 lb)
Max weight 410 kg (904 lb)
Water ballast None
Max wing loading 32.0 kg/m² (6.55 lb/sq ft)
Max speed 108 kt (200 km/h)
Stalling speed 36 kt (67 km/h)
Min sinking speed at 45 kt (83 km/h) 0.56 m (1.83 ft)/sec
Max rough air speed 108 kt (200 km/h)
Best glide ratio at 50 kt (93 km/h) 44

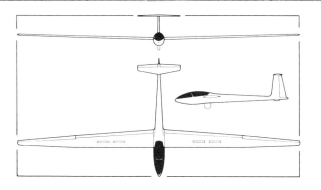

Akaflieg Darmstadt D-39 / West Germany

This unique single-seat powered sailplane, created by the Darmstadt Akaflieg, looks exactly like a Standard Class high-performance sailplane except for its low-mounted wing. Its great novelty, however, lies in the retractable two-blade folding propeller, driven by twin Fichtel & Sachs modified KM 914V engines situated in the nose cone.

The D-39 is an adaptation of the basic D-38 airframe, having the same glassfibre/balsa sandwich construction with ailerons of glassfibre/Klégécel foam sandwich, and Schempp-Hirth airbrakes on the upper wing surfaces. No flaps are fitted. It is equipped with a manually-retractable sprung monowheel, and accommodation comprises a semi-reclining seat under a flush canopy, the rear section of which is detachable. The D-39 first flew on 28 June 1979.

Data D-39
Manufacturer Akaflieg Darmstadt
First flight June 1979
Wing span 15.0 m (49 ft 2½ in)
Length 7.15 m (23 ft 5½ in)
Height 1.02 m (3 ft 4½ in)
Wing area 11.0 m² (118.4 sq ft)
Wing section Wortmann FX-61-184/60-126
Aspect ratio 20.5
Empty weight 280 kg (617 lb)
Max weight 400 kg (882 lb)
Water ballast None
Max wing loading 36.3 kg/m² (7.43 lb/sq ft)
Max speed 135 kt (250 km/h)
Stalling speed 39 kt (72 km/h)
Min sinking speed 1.0 m (3.3 ft)/sec
Best glide ratio at 56.5 kt (105 km/h) 36
Power plant 2 × Fichtel & Sachs KM 914V, 35 kW (47 hp)

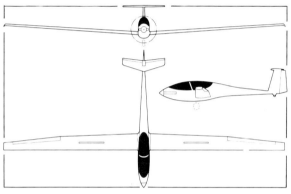

T-O run 200 m (656 ft)
Rate of climb at S/L 240 m (787 ft)/min
Range 500 km (269 nm)

West Germany / **Akaflieg München Mü 13**

The Mü series was developed from the two-seat Mü 10 Milan, which had been built at the Munich Akaflieg under the direction of Dipl.Ing. Scheibe. In 1935 and 1936 two prototypes, the Merlin and the Atalante, were built. The latter, with many improvements, went into series production at the Black Forest Aircraft works.

The Mü 13 is of mixed construction, using wood, steel and chrome-molybdenum-tin alloy, the metal and wood parts being connected with pop-rivets. The wooden cantilever wings incorporate steel-tube flaps and steel-framed fabric-covered ailerons. The fuselage is a fabric-covered steel-frame structure of square cross-section with a conventional wood tailplane and large windows inset into the sides of the cockpit.

From 1939 onwards many variations were introduced. Airbrakes replaced the flaps. The fuselage was altered so that the rear cross-section is triangular. At least four different canopies were used.

About 150 Mü 13s were produced and 1943 saw the Mü 13D-3 (photo below), with increased wing span and fuselage length and modified fin and rudder. In May 1939 Kurt Schmidt set a new German goal flight record of 482 km (260 nm) in a Mü 13 Atalante.

Data Mü 13 Atalante
Manufacturer Akaflieg München
First flight 1936
Wing span 16.0 m (52 ft 6 in)
Length 6.02 m (19 ft 9 in)
Wing area 16.16 m² (174 sq ft)
Wing section Mü
Aspect ratio 15.85
Empty weight 170 kg (375 lb)
Max weight 270 kg (595 lb)
Water ballast None
Max wing loading 16.71 kg/m² (3.42 lb/sq ft)
Max speed 108 kt (200 km/h)
Stalling speed 27 kt (50 km/h)
Min sinking speed at 29.5 kt (55 km/h) 0.6 m (2 ft)/sec
Best glide ratio at 35.5 kt (66 km/h) 28

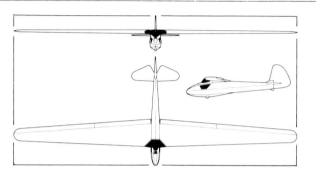

Akaflieg München Mü 27 / West Germany

The interest in variable-geometry wings has stimulated the German Akafliegs at the technical universities to attempt various solutions, which may in future have a significant effect on the design of high performance sailplanes. Stuttgart is using telescopic wings on the FS-29 and Munich, with their latest design, the Mü 27, are using slotted Fowler type flaps to increase and decrease wing area in flight. At high speeds a good glide angle is achieved by withdrawing the flaps, while at low speeds the wing area can be increased by 36% when the flaps are fully extended.

The Mü 27 is a tandem two-seat high performance sailplane. The fuselage is an all-glassfibre semi-monocoque structure with a large clear two-piece side-hinged canopy, a retractable monowheel and a fixed tail wheel. The cantilever T-tail is of glassfibre/foam sandwich and the wings are made of glassfibre/Conticell sandwich with aluminium spars and metal webs. The ailerons are linked to the flaps and the airbrakes at 50% chord operate on the upper surface. First flight of the Mü 27 took place at Oberpfaffenhofen on 24 February 1979, with Thomas Fischer at the controls.

Data Mü 27
Manufacturer Akaflieg München
First flight February 1979
Wing span 22.0 m (72 ft 2¼ in)
Length 10.3 m (33 ft 9½ in)
Height 1.8 m (5 ft 11 in)
Wing area 17.6-23.9 m² (189.5-257.3 sq ft)
Wing section Wortmann FX-67-VC-170/136
Aspect ratio 20.2-27.5
Empty weight 480 kg (1,058 lb)
Max weight 700 kg (1,543 lb)
Water ballast None
Max wing loading (flaps in) 40.0 kg/m² (8.19 lb/sq ft)
Max speed 151 kt (280 km/h)
Min sinking speed at 32.5 kt (60 km/h) 0.56 m (1.8 ft)/sec
Best glide ratio at 54.5 kt (101 km/h) 47

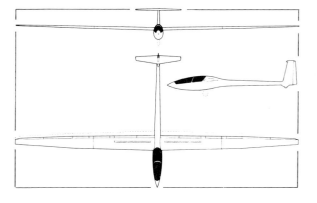

West Germany / **Akaflieg Stuttgart FS-24 Phönix**

The Phönix was the first sailplane to be built of glassfibre. Designed and built by Stuttgart Academic Flying Group under the direction of R. Eppler and H. Nägele, it was originally developed in 1951. The aim was to reduce weight rather than increase the wing area. For this purpose balsa wood with a stiffened outer skin of paper-and-glue layers was to be used, but the project was suspended. Fortunately the Group was able to get a subsidy which made further research possible and the project was completed.

By this time, glassfibre strengthened polyester resins were available. Balsa wood was retained as a filling material for the sandwich skin and glassfibre was used as an outer skin.

The monocoque fuselage is constructed in two pieces with a sandwich skin of glassfibre and balsa wood. The weight-carrying points and the rim of the canopy are strengthened with plywood. The wing attachment, controls and fittings are installed before the two pieces are glued together with overlapping glassfibre. The wings are constructed in a similar way. Ailerons, flaps and rudder are cut out after the gluing process.

The Phönix first flew on 27 November 1957. The conventional tail was subsequently replaced by a T-tail and retractable landing gear was incorporated. Eight examples of the Phönix were built, all of which are still flying.

Data   FS-24 Phönix-T
Manufacturer   Akaflieg Stuttgart
First flight   November 1957
Wing span   16.0 m (52 ft 6 in)
Length   6.84 m (22 ft 5¼ in)
Wing area   14.36 m² (154.6 sq ft)
Wing section   EC86(-3)-914
Aspect ratio   17.83
Empty weight   164 kg (362 lb)
Max weight   265 kg (584 lb)
Water ballast   None
Max wing loading   18.5 kg/m² (3.79 lb/sq ft)
Max speed   97 kt (180 km/h)
Stalling speed   31 kt (58 km/h)
Min sinking speed at 37 kt (69 km/h)   0.51 m (1.7 ft)/sec
Max rough air speed   54 kt (100 km/h)
Best glide ratio at 42 kt (78 km/h)   40

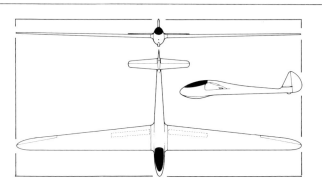

Akaflieg Stuttgart FS-29 / West Germany

A glider pilot's dream is to have polymorphic wings on his aircraft, automatically interchangeable in flight. These wings would have a high aspect ratio for thermalling and a low aspect ratio (and smaller area) for high-speed cross-country flying. Akaflieg Stuttgart is attempting to realise this ideal by the use of telescopic wings on its variable-geometry FS-29 sailplane. Designed in 1972, it first flew in June 1975.

The wings consist of outer telescopic sections which slide over inner fixed sections, thus varying the span. The inner wing comprises a box spar of glassfibre/Conticell foam sandwich. A stub spar protrudes to provide a mounting for the guide rails on which the outer panels move. Extension and retraction of the outer wing sections is manually operated by push-rods. The outer wing sections are of glassfibre/ foam/carbon-fibre sandwich. The wings incorporate plain ailerons of similar construction, and Schempp-Hirth airbrakes are fitted to the upper surfaces of the inner wings and are only effective when the outer panels are extended.

The fuselage is constructed of already available components, using the frame, canopy, landing gear and tail unit of a Schempp-Hirth Nimbus 2.

Data   FS-29
Manufacturer   Akaflieg Stuttgart
First flight   June 1975
Wing span   13.3-19.0 m (43 ft 7½ in-62 ft 4 in)
Length   7.16 m (23 ft 5¾ in)
Height   1.27 m (4 ft 2 in)
Wing area   8.56-12.65 m² (92.2-136.2 sq ft)
Wing section   Wortmann FX-73-170 (inner); FX-73-170/22 (outer)
Aspect ratio   20.67-28.54
Empty weight   357 kg (787 lb)
Max weight   450 kg (992 lb)
Water ballast   None
Max wing loading   52.6-35.6 kg/m² (10.77-7.29 lb/sq ft)
Max speed   135 kt (250 km/h)
Stalling speed   39 kt (72 km/h)
Min sinking speed at 40 kt (74 km/h)   0.54 m (1.8 ft)/sec
Max rough air speed   135 kt (250 km/h)

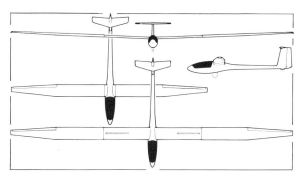

Best glide ratio at 54 kt (100 km/h)   44

West Germany / **Bölkow Phoebus**

The Phoebus is derived from the Phönix, the first all-glassfibre sailplane. The Phoebus is a joint design by H. Nägele, R. Linder and R. Eppler and was built by Bölkow at Ottobrun. It first flew on 4 April 1964. The main improvements over the Phönix are better high-speed performance, simplified control mechanism, a stronger skin, an all-moving T-tail and improved gust response. The adoption of the all-moving tail with no tabs reduces drag, weight and expense, and its high position avoids the downflow from the wing.

There are three versions of the Phoebus: models A, B and C. Model A, which made its first public appearance at the World Championships at South Cerney in 1965, is the Standard Class 15 metre version incorporating a fixed landing wheel. Model B, similar to the Model A but incorporating a retractable wheel, appeared two years later. The Phoebus C features a 17 metre wing, retractable wheel and tail brake parachute.

At the World Championships at Leszno, Poland, a Phoebus C, flown by Göran Ax of Sweden, was placed second and Rodolfo Hossinger of Argentina, also flying a Phoebus C, was sixth.

Production of the Phoebus series was discontinued in 1970 after 253 had been built.

Data Phoebus C
Manufacturer Bölkow
First flight April 1967
Wing span 17.0 m (55 ft 9¼ in)
Length 6.98 m (22 ft 10¾ in)
Wing area 14.06 m² (151.4 sq ft)
Wing section Eppler 403
Aspect ratio 20.55
Empty weight 235 kg (518 lb)
Max weight 375 kg (827 lb)
Water ballast None
Max wing loading 26.7 kg/m² (5.46 lb/sq ft)
Max speed 108 kt (200 km/h)
Stalling speed 31 kt (58 km/h)
Min sinking speed at 43 kt (80 km/h) 0.55m (1.8 ft)/sec
Max rough air speed 108 kt (200 km/h)
Best glide ratio at 48.5 kt (90 km/h) 42

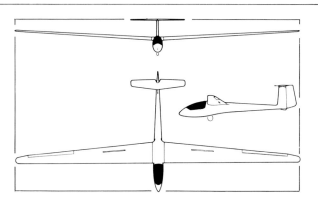

DFS Meise / West Germany

In the Spring of 1938, the International Olympic Committee decided to recognise gliding as an Olympic sport. The difficulty of judging sailplanes of many different types was to be overcome by stipulating standards to which competing aircraft had to conform; consequently the Fédération Aeronautique Internationale (FAI) announced a competition for the design of such an Olympic sailplane. The specifications were: span 15 m (49 ft 2½ in); empty weight 160 kg (353 lb); payload 95 kg (209 lb); maximum speed 200 km/h (110 kt); uniformity of building materials; fitted airbrakes; and no flaps or retractable undercarriage. The competition was held in February 1939 in Italy and entries included two from Italy – the A1 3 and Pellicano; two from Germany – the Meise and Mü 17 Merle; and one from Poland – the Orlik. Well-known pilots from several European countries test flew these aircraft. The Meise, designed by Hans Jacobs, was the final choice. For the few months before hostilities began many nations showed interest in this sailplane and the German Aero Club supplied details of the design. Many were built in other countries, some under different names. It was produced in Spain, in France as the Nord 2000, in Great Britain, where it was known as the EoN Olympia, and in Czechoslovakia, where it was designated the Zlin-25 Sohay.

Data Meise
Manufacturer DFS
First flight 1939
Wing span 15.0 m (49 ft 2½ in)
Length 7.27 m (23 ft 10¼ in)
Wing area 15.0 m² (161.5 sq ft)
Wing section Göttingen 549/676
Aspect ratio 15.0
Empty weight 160 kg (353 lb)
Max weight 255 kg (562 lb)
Water ballast None
Max wing loading 17.0 kg/m² (3.48 lb/sq ft)
Max speed 119 kt (220 km/h)
Stalling speed 29.5 kt (55 km/h)
Min sinking speed at 32 kt (59 km/h) 0.67 m (2.2 ft)/sec
Best glide ratio at 37 kt (69 km/h) 25.5

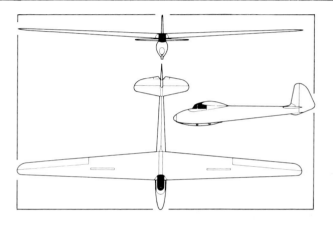

West Germany / **DFS Weihe**

The DFS Weihe, designed by Hans Jacob in 1938, proved to be a very popular sailplane and more than 350 were built in Germany, Sweden, France, Spain and Yugoslavia. It is a wooden aircraft and uses a thin aerofoil section. Instead of the gull wings of the Reiher, from which it was developed, it has straight wings for lower production costs. For rigging the wings are fitted into the fuselage with the wingtips on the ground; the tips are then raised and the wings locked into position with a bolt.

The fuselage is relatively long with a narrow cross section and though this improves its flying qualities it is at the expense of pilot comfort. The canopy was of the sectional type but the later Weihe 50, produced by Focke-Wulf in 1950, had a one-piece streamlined canopy.

The Weihe was placed fourth in the Rhön competition in 1938. In 1947 Per Axel Persson set a world height record of 8,050 m (26,411 ft), and in the 1948 World Championships 13 of the 29 competitors were flying Weihes. Even as late as 1952 and 1954 the Weihe was able to hold its own in international competitions in spite of the many new designs then appearing. In 1959, twenty years after its first flight, it set a world height record of 9,665 m (31,709 ft).

Data Weihe
Manufacturer DFS
First flight 1938
Wing span 18.0 m (59 ft 0½ in)
Length 8.3 m (27 ft 3 in)
Wing area 18.2 m² (195.9 sq ft)
Wing section Göttingen 549/676
Aspect ratio 17.8
Empty weight 190 kg (419 lb)
Max weight 325 kg (716 lb)
Water ballast None
Max wing loading 17.85 kg/m² (3.65 lb/sq ft)
Max speed 116 kt (215 km/h)
Stalling speed 24 kt (45 km/h)
Min sinking speed at 27 kt (50 km/h) 0.58 m (1.9 ft)/sec
Best glide ratio at 37.5 kt (70 km/h) 31

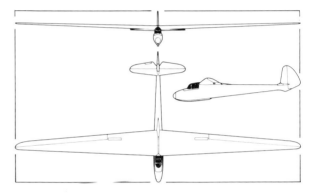

Glaser-Dirks DG-100 / West Germany

The D-38, predecessor to the DG-100, was designed at Akaflieg Darmstadt. It showed even better performance and handling qualities than had been expected and designer Wilhelm Dirks decided to develop a production version. He found a sponsor in private industry and with Gerhard Glaser formed the Glaser-Dirks Flugzeugbau.

The single-seat D-38 GRP (glass-reinforced-plastic) sailplane flew in February 1973 and only fifteen months later, on 10 May 1974, the prototype DG-100 was rolled out for its first flight. It is basically the same as the D-38 but has a better finish and the rounded nose of the D-38 has been replaced by an aerodynamically superior pointed nose.

Lighter plastic foam is used to support the glassfibre skin instead of the balsa of the D-38. The Wortmann FX-61-184 wing section is the best known aerofoil for flapless wings. Dirks had decided against flaps since they increase only slightly the average cross-country speed, and that only on good flying days; and because the powerful upper-surface Schempp-Hirth airbrakes are simpler to operate for landing, cheaper to make and save weight.

Glaser-Dirks have also built a number of examples of the DG-100G, which is generally similar to the DG-100 except that it has a tail unit similar to that of the DG-200.

Data DG-100
Manufacturer Glaser-Dirks
First flight May 1974
Wing span 15.0 m (49 ft 2½ in)
Length 7.0 m (22 ft 11½ in)
Height 1.4 m (4 ft 7 in)
Wing area 11.0 m² (118.4 sq ft)
Wing section Wortmann FX-61-184/60-126
Aspect ratio 20.5
Empty weight 230 kg (507 lb)
Max weight 418 kg (922 lb)
Water ballast 100 kg (220 lb)
Max wing loading 38.0 kg/m² (8.78 lb/sq ft)
Max speed 140 kt (260 km/h)
Stalling speed 32.5 kt (60 km/h)
Min sinking speed at 40 kt (74 km/h) 0.59 m (1.94 ft)/sec
Max rough air speed 140 kt (260 km/h)
Best glide ratio at 56.5 kt (105 km/h) 39.2

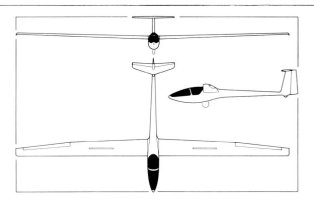

West Germany / **Glaser-Dirks DG-200**

Despite the success of the DG-100 there remains a demand for a sailplane with flaps for the 15 m Unrestricted Class international competitions, so Glaser-Dirks have embarked on the production of a second model, the DG-200, to satisfy this requirement. The same 15 metre wing span, long slim fuselage and T-tail are featured in the DG-200, but flaps have been added and the wing area reduced. The first flight was on 22 April 1977.

The tailplane on the prototype DG-100 was all-moving, incorporating a large anti-servo tab, but this was altered to a conventional fixed tailplane and elevator on both the DG-100 and DG-200. The trimmer is fitted on the control column, which is of the parallelogram linkage type, enabling high speed flight with reduced risk of pilot-induced oscillation.

The pilot is accommodated in semi-reclining position in the slim cockpit, covered by a two-piece canopy, the rear section of which is hinged to open upwards and back. The adjustable head rest is attached to the canopy hinge. The landing gear includes a retractable main wheel and a fixed tail wheel. A maximum of 120 kg (265 lb) of water ballast is carried.

In 1978 two other versions were developed: the 17 m DG-200-17 and the 13.1 m Acroracer, both with detachable wing tips to permit conversion to 15 m Class.

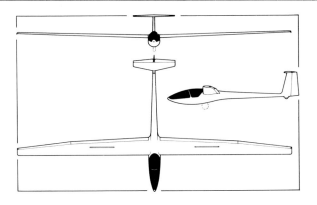

Data DG-200
Manufacturer Glaser-Dirks
First flight April 1977
Wing span 15.0 m (49 ft 2½ in)
Length 7.0 m (22 ft 11½ in)
Height 1.4 m (4 ft 7 in)
Wing area 10.0 m² (107.7 sq ft)
Wing section Wortmann FX-61-184/60-126
Aspect ratio 22.5
Empty weight 230 kg (507 lb)
Max weight 450 kg (992 lb)
Water ballast 120 kg (265 lb)
Max wing loading 45 kg/m² (9.22 lb/sq ft)
Max speed 146 kt (270 km/h)
Stalling speed 33.5 kt (62 km/h)
Min sinking speed at 39 kt (72 km/h) 0.55 m (1.8 ft)/sec
Max rough air speed 146 kt (270 km/h)
Best glide ratio at 59.5 kt (110 km/h) 42

Glasflügel BS 1 / West Germany

In 1962, Björn Stender, who worked on the SB-6 while a student at Brunswick Akaflieg, was commissioned to design and build a high performance sailplane by the South African Helli Lasch, and with three helpers started work on what was to be the BS 1.

This sailplane is built from glassfibre, and to keep the fuselage cross section as small as possible the pilot lies in the prone position. The T-tail incorporates a brake parachute and the wing features camber-changing flaps. The BS 1 was rolled out at the end of 1962. After many test flights the BS 1 broke the 300 km (162 nm) triangle record during the spring of 1963 and won several regional championships. It was regarded as a sailplane with one of the highest performances of its time.

Unhappily the brilliant young designer was killed while test flying in October 1963. Glasflügel then took over the project, modified the sailplane and produced it as the BS 1B. This version first flew on 24 May 1966. A new fuselage profile provides a more roomy cockpit, the wing span is increased and a new aerofoil section is used to improve performance in weak thermals.

Eighteen BS 1Bs were built, one aircraft being exported to England for naturalist and glider pilot Sir Peter Scott.

Data BS 1B
Manufacturer Glasflügel
First flight May 1966
Wing span 18.0 m (59 ft 0½ in)
Length 7.5 m (24 ft 7¼ in)
Height 1.54 m (5 ft 0½ in)
Wing area 14.1 m² (151.7 sq ft)
Wing section Eppler 348
Aspect ratio 23.0
Empty weight 335 kg (739 lb)
Max weight 460 kg (1,014 lb)
Water ballast None
Max wing loading 32.62 kg/m² (6.68 lb/sq ft)
Max speed 135 kt (250 km/h)
Stalling speed 35 kt (65 km/h)
Min sinking speed at 46 kt (85 km/h) 0.55 m (1.8 ft)/sec
Max rough air speed 135 kt (250 km/h)
Best glide ratio at 51 kt (95 km/h) 44

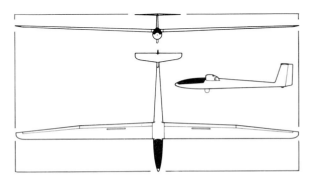

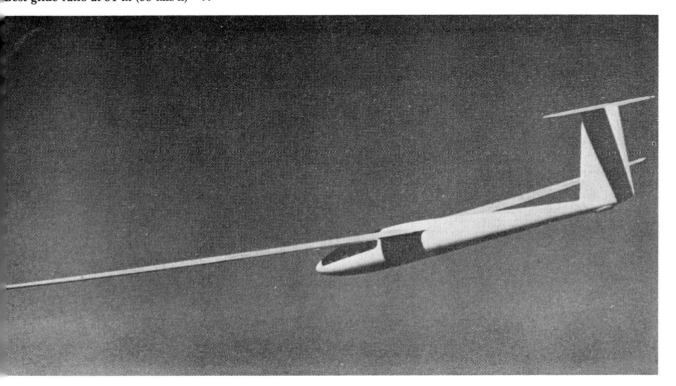

West Germany / **Glasflügel H 301 Libelle**

The H 301 Libelle is a compact single-seat all-glassfibre sailplane which had an immediate impact when it was introduced. It was developed by Eugen Hänle, who spent six years building the V-tailed H-30, and later headed the firm of Glasflügel, and by Dipl.Ing. W. Hütter, who was concerned in the design of many successful gliders, including the Minimoa, H-17 and H-28.

The Libelle (Dragonfly), which first flew on 6 March 1964, features camber-changing flaps and a manually retractable wheel, which put it in the Open class despite its small wing span. Its two-piece wings are constructed from GRP/balsa sandwich with glassfibre spars joined at the fuselage by a tongue-fork junction, which has since been widely adopted by other sailplane manufacturers. The Hütter airbrakes close firmly with a spring mechanism, preventing disturbed airflow. The leading edge contains a compartment for the water ballast.

The fuselage is an all-glassfibre shell with balsa and synthetic foam. The pilot sits in a semi-reclining position under a shallow canopy, giving good all-round visibility, and the resulting smaller surface area at the nose decreases frontal drag.

Production of the H 301 was discontinued in 1969 in favour of the Standard Libelle and Kestrel 17.

Data Libelle 301
Manufacturer Glasflügel
First flight March 1964
Wing span 15.0 m (49 ft 2½ in)
Length 6.2 m (20 ft 4 in)
Wing area 9.50 m² (102.25 sq ft)
Wing section Hütter
Aspect ratio 23.6
Empty weight 180 kg (397 lb)
Max weight 300 kg (661 lb)
Water ballast 50 kg (110 lb)
Max wing loading 31.25 kg/m² (6.4 lb/sq ft)
Max speed 135 kt (250 km/h)
Stalling speed 35 kt (65 km/h)
Min sinking speed at 40.5 kt (75 km/h) 0.55 m (1.8 ft)/sec
Max rough air speed 86.5 kt (160 km/h)
Best glide ratio at 51 kt (95 km/h) 39

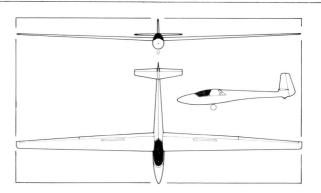

Glasflügel H 201 Standard Libelle / West Germany

The successful Open Class Libelle, which won so many National championships and broke world speed and distance records, was the precursor of the popular Standard Libelle and Kestrel 17. The Standard Libelle, as its name implies, was produced to comply with the requirements of the Standard Class. The main changes made to the H 301 Libelle to produce the Standard Libelle were originally the fitting of a fixed landing wheel, raising the height of the canopy and dispensing with the flaps and tail parachute. However, with the change in Standard Class rules in 1970, a retractable wheel was substituted. Like the H 301 Libelle, it is constructed from glassfibre, beautifully made and easy to

rig. Both sailplanes have many cockpit refinements such as an inflatable knee cushion, and back rest and rudder pedals adjustable in flight. One ingenious feature of the canopy is a catch that allows the front to be raised by 25 mm in flight to provide a blast of ventilation when required.

The first flight was made in 1967 and by the time production ended in the mid-1970s more than 600 Standard Libelles had been built. A year after its maiden flight the Standard Libelle took second place in the World Championships at Leszno in Poland, flown by Axel Persson.

Data Standard Libelle 201B
Manufacturer Glasflügel
First flight October 1967
Wing span 15.0 m (49 ft 2½ in)
Length 6.2 m (20 ft 4 in)
Height 1.31 m (4 ft 4 in)
Wing area 9.8 m² (105.5 sq ft)
Wing section Wortmann FX-66-17A-11-182
Aspect ratio 23.0
Empty weight 185 kg (408 lb)
Max weight 350 kg (772 lb)
Water ballast 50 kg (110 lb)
Max wing loading 35.7 kg/m² (7.31 lb/sq ft)
Max speed 135 kt (250 km/h)
Stalling speed 33.5 kt (62 km/h)
Min sinking speed at 40 kt (75 km/h) 0.60 m (1.96 ft)/sec
Max rough air speed 135 kt (250 km/h)
Best glide ratio at 46 kt (85 km/h) 38

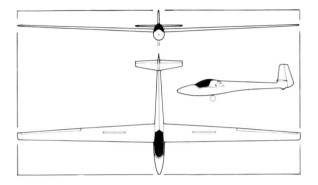

West Germany / **Glasflügel 205 Club Libelle**

The Standard Libelle and Libelle proved to be such popular sailplanes that Glasflügel decided to produce a new model with the specific aims of suiting club training methods through good handling characteristics, especially easy away-landing for inexperienced pilots; suitability for advanced cross-country training up to Diamond standard; and suitability for conversion training to modern high performance glassfibre sailplanes in both classes.

The design of the Club Libelle is based on that of the Standard Libelle. It is a shoulder-wing sailplane of glassfibre/plastic construction. The new two-piece double-tapered wings are of GRP foam section with spar flanges of parallel glassfibre and webs in GRP-balsa. They incorporate trailing edge flaps/airbrakes which run the full length from the wingroot to the ailerons.

The fuselage is an all-glassfibre monocoque structure; no sandwich construction is used. The cockpit, which is more roomy than that of the Standard Libelle, is covered by a clear one-piece canopy. The back rest and rudder pedals are adjustable.

Unlike the Standard Libelle, the Club Libelle has a T-tail, and the landing gear, consisting of a main wheel with brake is non-retractable.

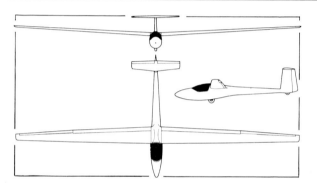

Data   Club Libelle
Manufacturer   Glasflügel
First flight   September 1973
Wing span   15.0 m (49 ft 2½ in)
Length   6.4 m (21 ft 0 in)
Height   1.4 m (4 ft 7 in)
Wing area   9.8 m² (105.5 sq ft)
Wing section   Wortmann FX-66-17A-11-182
Aspect ratio   23.0
Empty weight   200 kg (441 lb)
Max weight   330 kg (727 lb)
Water ballast   None
Max wing loading   33.67 kg/m² (6.89 lb/sq ft)
Max speed   108 kt (200 km/h)
Stalling speed   32.5 kt (60 km/h)
Min sinking speed at 36.5 kt (67 km/h)   0.56 m (1.84 ft) sec
Max rough air speed   108 kt (200 km/h)
Best glide ratio at 48.5 kt (90 km/h)   35

Glasflügel 206 Hornet / West Germany

The Hornet single-seat high-performance sailplane is a development of the popular Club Libelle and successor to the Standard Libelle. It was developed to meet the new Standard Class requirements, which permit retractable landing gear and water ballast.

Derived from the Club Libelle, the Hornet is similarly all-glassfibre in construction. The wings have been lowered from the shoulder to the mid-set position and the incidence changed to improve performance at high speeds. They have also been strengthened to accommodate water tanks carrying a total of 120 litres. The powerful trailing-edge airbrakes are shortened by 0.46 m (18 in) at the wing roots.

The nose section is modified to take a more streamlined two-piece canopy, the aft section of which opens upwards for access. The landing gear consists of a retractable unsprung monowheel with brake, and a tailwheel.

The Hornet first flew at Saulgau on 21 December 1974 and 90 examples had been produced by summer 1979. The same year saw the introduction of the Hornet C, featuring carbon-fibre wings which reduced the empty weight by 20 kg (44 lb), allowing the water ballast capacity to be increased to 170 kg (375 lb). The glassfibre fuselage has the one-piece Mosquito canopy, and the wing-root fairings are modified.

Data Hornet
Manufacturer Glasflügel
First flight December 1974
Wing span 15.0 m (49 ft 2½ in)
Length 6.4 m (21 ft 0 in)
Height 1.4 m (4 ft 7 in)
Wing area 9.80 m² (105.5 sq ft)
Wing section Wortmann FX-67-K-150
Aspect ratio 23.0
Empty weight 227 kg (500 lb)
Max weight 420 kg (926 lb)
Water ballast 120 kg (265 lb)
Max wing loading 42.9 kg/m² (8.8 lb/sq ft)
Max speed 135 kt (250 km/h)
Stalling speed 36 kt (67 km/h)
Min sinking speed at 40.5 kt (75 km/h) 0.60 m (1.97 ft)/sec
Best glide ratio at 56 kt (103 km/h) 38

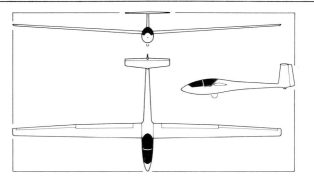

West Germany / **Glasflügel 401 Kestrel 17**

Following the success of the Libelle series Glasflügel decided in 1968 on a new design which would satisfy pilots who wanted a sailplane like the Libelle but with a longer wingspan and a more roomy cockpit. On 9 August 1968, the prototype Kestrel was first flown at Karlsruhe-Forchheim and went into production in 1969.

This single-seat high performance Open Class sailplane with camber-changing flaps and retractable landing wheel was designed by the team of Hänle and Prasser, advised by Dr Althaus of Stuttgart University. The fixed T-tail is secured with three attachments and the elevator is operated by two prongs on the rear attachments. The glassfibre fuselage, in its original form, did have a small flow separation at the wing root junction at low speeds, but this has been cured by adding large fillets, which are also used on the Kestrel 19. The two-piece glassfibre and balsa wings incorporate camber-changing flaps which operate in conjunction with the ailerons between −8° and +12° and can be lowered to +35° for landing. For short-field landings a brake parachute located in the tail and flush-fitting airbrakes on the top surface of the wings are provided.

The drawing shows the original Kestrel design. For later modifications see the Slingsby T.59 Kestrel 19 (page 166).

Data   Kestrel 17
Manufacturer   Glasflügel
First flight   August 1968
Wing span   17.0 m (55 ft 9¼ in)
Length   6.72 m (22 ft 0½ in)
Height   1.52 m (5 ft 0 in)
Wing area   11.6 m² (124.9 sq ft)
Wing section   Wortmann FX-67-K-170/150
Aspect ratio   25.0
Empty weight   260 kg (573 lb)
Max weight   400 kg (882 lb)
Water ballast   45 kg (99 lb)
Max wing loading   34.5 kg/m² (7.06 lb/sq ft)
Max speed   135 kt (250 km/h)
Stalling speed   33.5 kt (63 km/h)
Min sinking speed at 40 kt (74 km/h)   0.55 m (1.8 ft)/sec
Max rough air speed   135 kt (250 km/h)
Best glide ratio at 52.5 kt (97 km/h)   43

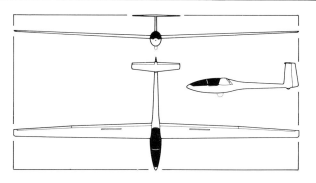

Glasflügel 604 / West Germany

The Glasflügel 604 is a single-seat 22 metre version of the Kestrel 17. It has been flown with great success in competitions and has established several World and national records including the ladies' speed record set by Adele Orsi of Italy over a 100 km (54 nm) triangle, averaging 120.153 km/h (64.84 kt). Only ten 604s have been produced. Originally designed as a study for a projected two-seat high performance sailplane, the Glasflügel 604 was built in only four months, from January to April 1970, and the aircraft was entered for the 1970 World Championships at Marfa, Texas, where it was placed sixth. In the 1974 World Championships in Australia it took second place.

The Glasflügel 604 is similar in appearance and construction to the Kestrel 17. The 604, however, has a three-piece wing with the centre section incorporating the fuselage top, and the outer panels joined to the centre section by the Hütter-Hänle method. The difficulties in directional control encountered with large span aircraft are overcome by an increase in fuselage length of 1.65 m (5 ft 5 in). The new hinged cockpit canopy has less transparency area than that of the Kestrel 17 and opens upwards and aft. Landing gear consists of a manually retractable monowheel with brake and fixed tailwheel.

Data 604
Manufacturer Glasflügel
First flight April 1970
Wing span 22.0 m (72 ft 2 in)
Length 7.6 m (24 ft 11¼ in)
Height 1.67 m (5 ft 5¾ in)
Wing area 16.23 m² (174.7 sq ft)
Wing section Wortmann FX-67-K-170/150
Aspect ratio 29.8
Empty weight 440 kg (992 lb)
Max weight 650 kg (1,433 lb)
Water ballast 100 kg (220 lb)
Max wing loading 40 kg/m² (8.6 lb/sq ft)
Max speed 135 kt (250 km/h)
Stalling speed 34.5 kt (64 km/h)
Min sinking speed at 39 kt (72 km/h) 0.5 m (1.64 ft)/sec
Max rough air speed 135 kt (250 km/h)
Best glide ratio at 53 kt (98 km/h) 49

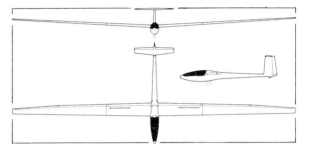

West Germany / **Glasflügel 303 Mosquito**

The Mosquito was the first sailplane to be produced under the new name of Holighaus and Hillenbrand. Following the death on 21 September 1975 of Ing. Eugen Hänle, director of Glasflügel, Klaus Holighaus of Schempp-Hirth and Hillenbrand of Glasflügel formed a partnership which resulted in the world's largest production capacity of sailplanes.

Developed from the Standard Class Hornet, the Mosquito is an Unrestricted 15 m Class sailplane. An interesting feature is the new type of airbrake/flap combination developed jointly by Holighaus and Hänle. These flaps are a combination of ordinary trailing-edge flaps and rear-edge rotating brake flaps. The normal flap level operates the trailing-edge flap and droops the ailerons. There is a second level for the brake flap, the effect of which is to partly open the brake flap on the upper surface of the wing. As the lever is pulled back, the brake flap opens further while at the same time the trailing-edge flap moves further downwards. In normal landing the brake flap, when fully extended, operates like a brake parachute but can be opened or closed at any time, as a Schempp-Hirth airbrake, without the aircraft stalling.

Data Mosquito B
Manufacturer Glasflügel
First flight February 1976
Wing span 15.0 m (49 ft 2½ in)
Length 6.39 m (20 ft 11½ in)
Height 1.4 m (4 ft 7 in)
Wing area 9.86 m² (106.1 sq ft)
Wing section Wortmann FX-67-K-150
Aspect ratio 23.0
Empty weight 235 kg (518 lb)
Max weight 450 kg (992 lb)
Water ballast 120 kg (265 lb)
Max wing loading 46 kg/m² (9.72 lb/sq ft)
Max speed 135 kt (250 km/h)
Stalling speed 36 kt (66 km /h)
Min sinking speed at 43 kt (80 km/h) 0.57 m (1.87 ft)/sec
Max rough air speed 135 kt (250 km/h)
Best glide ratio at 59 kt (110 km/h) 42

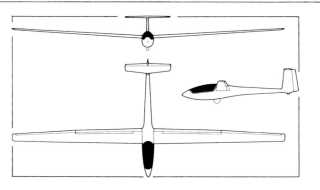

Grob G-102 Astir CS 77 / West Germany

The Astir CS (Club Standard) is a single-seat high-performance 15 metre sailplane, manufactured by Burkhart Grob. The Astir CS is designed for clubs as well as private owners who require an easy-to-fly glassfibre sailplane with a large roomy cockpit.

The large wing area of this aircraft is one of its striking features and has led to improvements in low speed performance.

Construction of the Astir (photo below) began in March 1974 and the prototype flew for the first time on 19 December 1974; it entered production in July 1975. It is of all-glassfibre construction with a long fuselage and a T-tail. It incorporates a sprung retractable landing wheel. The water ballast is carried in the flapless wings with the dump valve in the fuselage. Rigging is achieved without the need for any separate removable parts as the wings and tailplane are attached by an ingenious system of 'snap-lock' connectors. After 534 had been produced the current version, the CS 77 with a new, slimmer and longer fuselage, went into production in spring 1977, followed by the Club Astir, with fixed undercarriage, in summer 1977. Some 395 of these two models had been produced by the end of 1978.

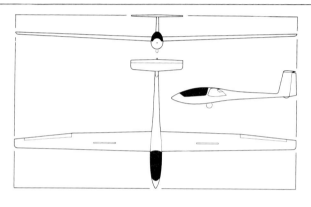

Data G-102 Astir CS 77
Manufacturer Burkhart Grob
First flight December 1974
Wing span 15.0 m (49 ft 2½ in)
Length 6.69 m (21 ft 11¼ in)
Height 1.4 m (4 ft 7 in)
Wing area 12.4 m² (133.5 sq ft)
Wing section Eppler E603
Aspect ratio 18.2
Empty weight 270 kg (595 lb)
Max weight 450 kg (992 lb)
Water ballast 100 kg (220 lb)
Max wing loading 36.3 kg/m² (7.43 lb/sq ft)
Max speed 135 kt (250 km/h)
Stalling speed 32.5 kt (60 km/h)
Min sinking speed at 40.5 kt (75 km/h) 0.6 m (2 ft)/sec
Max rough air speed 135 kt (250 km/h)
Best glide ratio at 56.5 kt (105 km/h) 38

West Germany / **Grob G-103 Twin Astir**

The Twin Astir is the high-performance two-seat companion of the Astir CS and is of similar construction. Design and prototype construction began in September 1974 and March 1976 respectively, and the prototype flew for the first time on 31 December 1976.

Grob decided that, unlike many two-seaters which have fixed landing gear, the Twin Astir should have a retractable landing wheel. This poses problems because the rear seat, which is sited on the centre of gravity, takes up the available space. Consequently a new method of retracting the wheel into a smaller space had to be devised. The wheel rotates through 90° sideways, thus fitting the undercarriage horizontally under the rear seat.

Like the Astir CS, the Twin Astir is of glassfibre construction with T-tail. The two seats are arranged in tandem with dual controls under two individual canopies. The Twin Astir is marketed with or without water ballast and basic instruments in the front cockpit. By the end of 1978 a total of 225 Twin Astirs had been delivered.

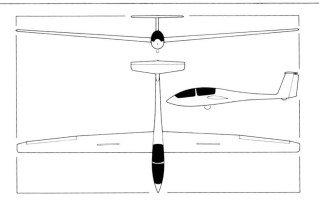

Data G-103 Twin Astir
Manufacturer Burkhart Grob
First flight December 1976
Wing span 17.5 m (57 ft 5 in)
Length 8.1 m (26 ft 6¾ in)
Height 1.6 m (5 ft 3 in)
Wing area 17.9 m² (192.7 sq ft)
Wing section Eppler E603
Aspect ratio 17.1
Empty weight 390 kg (860 lb)
Max weight 620 kg (1,367 lb)
Water ballast 90 kg (198 lb)
Max wing loading 34.6 kg/m² (7.08 lb/sq ft)
Max speed 135 kt (250 km/h)
Stalling speed 40 kt (74 km/h)
Min sinking speed at 40 kt (75 km/h) 0.62 m (2.0 ft)/sec
Max rough air speed 108 kt (200 km/h)
Best glide ratio at 59.5 kt (110 km/h) 38

Grob Speed Astir II / West Germany

After three years of development, Grob brought out the high-performance single-seat 15 m Unrestricted Class Speed Astir II in the summer of 1978. Many technical innovations have been introduced. The slender new laminar-flow fuselage of oval cross-section incorporates carbon-fibre reinforcements in high-stress areas. The cockpit was lengthened by 20 cm (7.87 in) in October 1979 to accommodate tall pilots. It features a two-piece canopy, the rear section of which is hinged to open aft. The tail unit is similar to that of the Astir CS but with shorter fin and rudder, and the new tailplane has a sealed elevator hinge line.

The use of carbon-fibre in the wing spars results in added strength and weight savings. The slotless flaps extend half-way along the trailing edges, and the ailerons, which can be deflected in the same way, continue to the wingtips. Mounted on tracks and rollers, the ailerons and flaps articulate with the lower wing surface and can slightly increase the wing area. The wing upper surface features 'elastic' strips which form a permanent seal between flap and wing.

Data Speed Astir II
Manufacturer Burkhart Grob
First flight April 1978
Wing span 15.0 m (49 ft 2½ in)
Length 6.60 m (21 ft 8 in)
Height 1.27 m (4 ft 2 in)
Wing area 11.5 m² (124.8 sq ft)
Wing section Eppler E660
Aspect ratio 19.6
Empty weight 250 kg (551 lb)
Max weight 515 kg (1,134 lb)
Water ballast 180 kg (397 lb)
Max wing loading 45 kg/m² (9.2 lb/sq ft)
Max speed 146 kt (270 km/h)
Stalling speed 35 kt (64 km/h)
Min sinking speed at 40 kt (75 km/h) 0.57 m (1.87 ft)/sec
Best glide ratio at 65 kt (120 km/h) 41.5

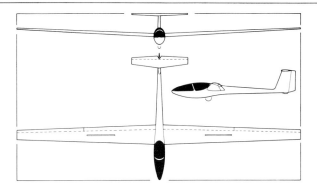

West Germany / **ISF Mistral C**

In 1977 Dipl Ing Manfred Strauber and his associates – who designed and built the Standard Class Mistral, which first flew in 1975 – produced the Mistral C to comply with the new FAI Club regulations. Introduced in 1975 to open up international competitions to a wider range of entries, the Club Class is characterised by limitations on size, including the wing span, fixed landing gear and the lack of camber-changing flaps and water ballast. The Mistral, a robust glider with good flying qualities, is also suitable for use by pilots at all stages of experience, from first solo to competition entry. The glassfibre fuselage of the Mistral C features a roomy cockpit capable of housing pilots of all sizes,

and a one-piece canopy hinged to open sideways gives good all-round vision. The rudder pedals are adjustable. A tow hook is sited at the centre of gravity; a nose hook, for aerotowing, is optional.

The shoulder wings and T-tail are of glassfibre and Conticell sandwich construction. The wings incorporate large ailerons and have very effective airbrakes on the upper surface. The T-tail has a fixed-incidence tailplane with spring-trim elevator. The landing gear comprises a large monowheel with brake, and a tailskid.

The Mistral C gained third place in a field of 33 in the first international Club competition, held in Sweden in 1979.

Data   Mistral C
Manufacturer   ISF (Ingenieur-Büro Strauber/Frommhold)
First flight   1977
Wing span   15.0 m (49 ft 2½ in)
Length   6.73 m (22 ft 1 in)
Height   1.45 m (4 ft 8 in)
Wing area   10.9 m² (117.3 sq ft)
Wing section   Wortmann FX-61-163
Aspect ratio   20.7
Empty weight   230 kg (510 lb)
Max weight   350 kg (772 lb)
Water ballast   None
Max wing loading   32 kg/m² (6.55 lb/sq ft)
Max speed   135 kt (250 km/h)
Stalling speed   33 kt (62 km/h)
Min sinking speed at 35 kt (65 km/h)   0.60 m (1.96 ft)/sec
Best glide ratio at 49 kt (90 km/h)   35

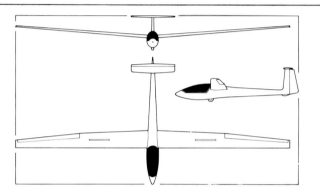

Kortenbach & Rauh Kora 1 / West Germany

The Kora 1 is a side-by-side two-seat twin-boom motor glider designed by Herren Schultes, Seidel and Putz and built by Kortenbach and Rauh of West Germany. Its power plant is a 65 hp Limbach air-cooled SL 1700 EC1 engine driving a Hoffmann two-blade variable-pitch feathering propeller and fitted aft of the cockpit.

The cantilever high-set wings are of all-wood construction with Schempp-Hirth airbrakes on the upper surfaces. The undercarriage consists of two main wheels set on thin steel sprung legs cantilevered from the fuselage nacelle and a forward-retracting nosewheel. On the first prototype the main wheels retracted into the twin booms. Side-by-side seating for two people is in a roomy cockpit 120 cm (47 in) wide under a fully-transparent canopy which opens sideways to starboard.

The first prototype flew in the Autumn of 1972, confirming the design to be sound, but the manufacturers decided that a more simplified version incorporating some weight saving was necessary for the production model, so a second prototype, the Kora 1-V2, was built and first flew on 9 April 1976.

Data Kora 1-V2
Manufacturer Kortenbach & Rauh
First flight April 1976
Wing span 18.0 m (59 ft 0½ in)
Length 7.4 m (24 ft 3½ in)
Height 1.85.m (6 ft 0¾ in)
Wing area 19.44 m² (209.3 sq ft)
Wing section Wortmann FX-66-S-196/161
Aspect ratio 16.65
Empty weight 510 kg (1,124 lb)
Max weight 750 kg (1,653 lb)
Water ballast None
Max wing loading 38.58 kg/m² (7.9 lb/sq ft)
Max level speed at S/L 110 kt (205 km/h)
Stalling speed 35 kt (65 km/h)
Min sinking speed at 51 kt (95 km/h) 0.85 m (2.8 ft)/sec
Best glide ratio at 54 kt (100 km/h) 30
Power plant Limbach SL 1700 EC1, 48.5 kW (65 hp)

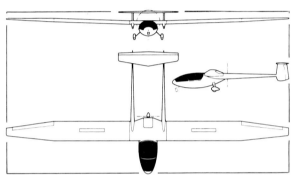

Max rate of climb at S/L 180 m (590 ft)/min

West Germany / **LCF 2**

The LCF 2 is a single-seat shoulder-wing sailplane constructed from mixed materials. It is a versatile aircraft, suitable for training, performance and aerobatic flying. It was built during 1970 and 1971 at Friedrichshafen as a successor to the LO 100 by a group of enthusiasts under the direction of Ing. Görgl and G. Kramper, taking about 4,000 working hours. It first flew on 22 March 1975. On the occasion of the 25th anniversary of the Friedrichshafen Aero Club it was christened *Kobold*, the Goblin. It was awarded first prize at the 1975 meeting of the Oscar-Ursinus Association (the German EAA).

The oval-section fuselage is a steel-tube frame with a glassfibre shell covering the nose section and fabric at the rear. The roomy cockpit is covered by a one-piece flush-fitting canopy, and this sailplane features a fixed landing wheel. The conventional tail is a Conticell/plywood structure. The single-spar wings are plywood covered and incorporate Schempp-Hirth airbrakes on the upper surfaces. The LCF 2 is suitable for amateur constructors or can be obtained ready built.

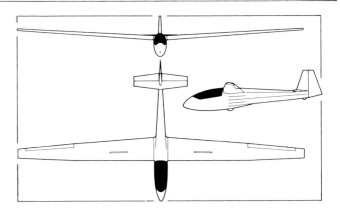

Data LCF 2
Manufacturer Scheibe
First flight March 1975
Wing span 13.0 m (42 ft 7¾ in)
Length 6.35 m (20 ft 10 in)
Height 0.9 m (2 ft 11½ in)
Wing area 10.0 m ² (107.7 sq ft)
Wing section Wortmann FX-60-126
Aspect ratio 16.9
Empty weight 190 kg (419 lb)
Max weight 300 kg (661 lb)
Water ballast None
Max wing loading 30.0 kg/m² (6.14 lb/sq ft)
Max speed 135 kt (250 km/h)
Stalling speed 33.5 kt (62 km/h)
Min sinking speed at 36.5 kt (68 km/h) 0.7 m (2.3 ft)/sec
Max rough air speed 135 kt (250 km/h)
Best glide ratio at 46 kt (68 km/h) 30.5

Rhein-Flugzeugbau Sirius 2 / West Germany

The Sirius 1 was developed to investigate the efficiency of the ducted fan as a means of propulsion for motor gliders. It was developed from the VFW FK-3 all-metal sailplane and was first powered by a Nelson 48 hp two-stroke engine, then by two Yamaha motor cycle engines and finally two 20 hp Fichtel & Sachs Wankel engines were chosen.

The Sirius 2 is the two-seat companion to the Sirius 1, but Rhein-Flugzeugbau, the manufacturers, in this case have arranged with Caproni of Italy to use the wings, tail unit and landing gear of the A-21 Calif.

This side-by-side two-seat ducted fan motor glider is powered by two 30 hp Wankel rotary engines which drive a ducted fan embedded in the fuselage just aft of the wing trailing edge. One engine is mounted in front of the fan and the other behind it. The fan shroud utilises an annular slat intake round the wing leading edge to keep the airflow attached to the duct, and suck-in doors fair off this intake when the power plant is not operating to maintain gliding performance.

Data Sirius 2
Manufacturer Rhein-Flugzeugbau
First flight January 1972
Wing span 20.38 m (66 ft 10½ in)
Length 8.04 m (26 ft 4½ in)
Height 1.8 m (5 ft 11 in)
Wing area 16.1 m² (173 sq ft)
Wing section Wortmann FX-67-K-170/60-126
Aspect ratio 25.8
Empty weight 510 kg (1,124 lb)
Max weight 690 kg (1,521 lb)
Water ballast None
Max wing loading 43.4 kg/m² (8.88 lb/sq ft)
Max speed (powered) 146 kt (270 km/h)
Stalling speed 39 kt (72 km/h)
Min sinking speed 0.6 m (2 ft)/sec
Best glide ratio 38
Power plant 2 × Wankel driving ducted fan

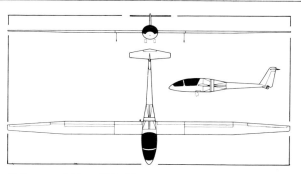

T-O run 200 m (656 ft)
Rate of climb 120 m (394 ft)/min
Range 270 km (147 nm)

West Germany / **Rolladen-Schneider LS1**

A significant German sailplane of the late 1960s was the LS1 series, designed by Dipl.Ing. Wolf Lemke and built by Walter Schneider. Two prototypes flew in the German Championships of 1968 and took the first two places out of forty-four competitors, thus becoming the top German Standard Class sailplane of that time.

Construction is of glassfibre and PVC foam. The 15 metre wings of the prototype were fitted with unusual airbrakes, consisting of an upward-hinging portion of the trailing edge inboard of the ailerons. This was hinged close to its mid-chord line so that the leading edge of the airbrake moved down while the trailing edge moved upwards. It was found, however, that they were only effective at certain speeds, so production models incorporated conventional Schempp-Hirth airbrakes.

The LS1 was produced in several versions: the LS1-c with all-moving tailplane and LS1-d with water ballast being two, of which more than 200 were built. The LS1-f has a redesigned rudder (of equal area to earlier versions) and a fixed tailplane with elevator. The fixed undercarriage has given way to retractable landing gear. Other improvements include rubber shock absorbers for the landing wheel and modifications to the tow release and cockpit interior.

Data LS1-f
Manufacturer Rolladen-Schneider
First flight 1972
Wing span 15.0 m (49 ft 2½ in)
Length 6.7 m (21 ft 11¾ in)
Height 1.2 m (3 ft 11½ in)
Wing area 9.75 m² (105 sq ft)
Wing section Wortmann FX-66-S-196 mod
Aspect ratio 23.0
Empty weight 200 kg (507 lb)
Max weight 390 kg (860 lb)
Water ballast 90 kg (198 lb)
Max wing loading 40 kg/m² (8.2 lb/sq ft)
Max speed 135 kt (220 km/h)
Stalling speed 33.5 kt (62 km/h)
Min sinking speed at 38 kt (70 km/h) 0.65 m (2.1 ft)/sec
Max rough air speed 135 kt (220 km/h)
Best glide ratio at 48.5 kt (90 km/h) 38

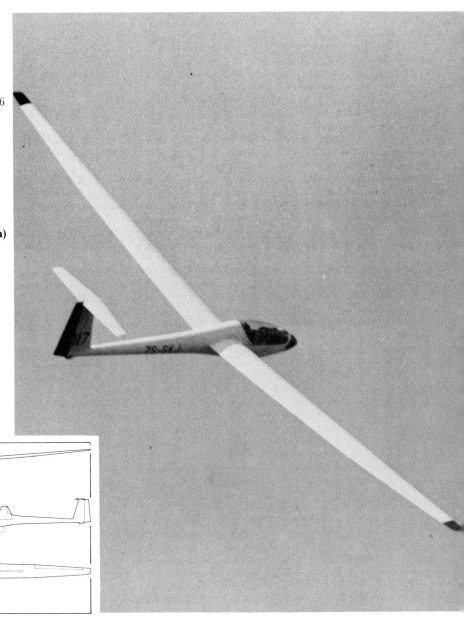

Rolladen-Schneider LS3A / West Germany

The championship winning design of the LS1, which may be said to be one of the second generation of glassfibre sailplanes, is almost ten years old; the LS2, which won the 1974 World Championships, never went into quantity production, and now Wolf Lemke and Walter Schneider have designed the LS3, built by Rolladen-Schneider. Design and construction of the LS3 began in 1975 and the aircraft first flew on 4 February 1976 at Egelsbach, Germany. This single-seat high performance 15 metre sailplane has cantilever mid-set wings of glassfibre/foam sandwich construction. One-piece flaperons ran the entire length of the trailing edge but were replaced by conventional flaps and ailerons in 1979. Airbrakes operate on the upper wing surfaces and there is provision for 120 kg (265 lb) of water ballast.

The fuselage, similar to that of the LS1-f, features a flush one-piece hinged canopy and T-tail with fixed tailplane with elevator. Landing gear consists of a monowheel with rubber shock absorber which is located 25 mm forward of the centre of gravity. An innovation is the mechanism which automatically prevents opening of the airbrakes at the incorrect flap setting. The LS3A-17 is a 17 m version with detachable wingtips for conversion to a 15 m sailplane.

Data LS3A
Manufacturer Rolladen-Schneider
First flight February 1976
Wing span 15.0 m (49 ft 2½ in)
Length 6.8 m (22 ft 3¾ in)
Height 1.2 m (3 ft 11¼ in)
Wing area 10.2 m² (109.8 sq ft)
Wing section Wortmann
Aspect ratio 22.0
Empty weight 246 kg (542 lb)
Max weight 470 kg (1,036 lb)
Water ballast 120 kg (265 lb)
Max wing loading 46.0 kg/m² (8.19 lb/sq ft)
Max speed 135 kt (250 km/h)
Stalling speed 35 kt (65 km/h)
Min sinking speed at 38 kt (70 km/h) 0.55 m (1.8 ft)/sec
Max rough air speed 135 kt (250 km/h)
Best glide ratio at 59 kt (110 km/h) 40

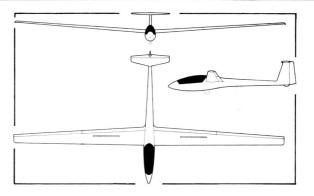

West Germany / **Scheibe Bergfalke 4**

The Bergfalke 4 is a two-seat high-performance sailplane designed by Egon Scheibe and is a development of the 1951 Mü 13E Bergfalke and its improved versions, Bergfalke 2 and 3. Construction of the prototype began in early 1969 with the first flight following a few months later. Because of its excellent performance the Bergfalke 4 can be used for competition flying as well as for training. The low sink rate makes it possible to soar in relatively weak thermals.

Great importance has been attached to ease and speed of rigging. The two-piece wings are of wooden construction with a single laminated box spar joined together at the fuselage centre-line with one vertical pin. The wing leading edge is covered with birch ply with fabric aft of the main spar. Large Schempp-Hirth airbrakes are fitted.

The fuselage is of tubular steel construction with a glassfibre nose section; the remainder is fabric covered. The landing gear consists of a large non-retractable monowheel fitted with a brake. The tailplane is wood with a Flettner-type trim tab on the elevator and is located by three spigots and secured by a nut.

In 1976, two versions of the Bergfalke 4 were entered for the Sixth German Motor Glider Competition: the twin-engined version and the retractable-engine version, which later put up a world 300 km triangle record.

Data Bergfalke 4
Manufacturer Scheibe
First flight 1969
Wing span 17.2 m (56 ft 5 in)
Length 8.00 m (26 ft 3 in)
Height 1.5 m (4 ft 11 in)
Wing area 17.5 m² (188 sq ft)
Wing section Wortmann SO2/SO2/1
Aspect ratio 16.9
Empty weight 300 kg (661 lb)
Max weight 505 kg (1,113 lb)
Water ballast None
Max wing loading 29.4 kg/m² (6.02 lb/sq ft)
Max speed 108 kt (200 km/h)
Stalling speed 35 kt (65 km/h)
Min sinking speed at 40.5 kt (75 km/h) 0.68 m (2.2 ft)/sec
Max rough air speed 92 kt (170 km/h)
Best glide at ratio at 46 kt (85 km/h) 34

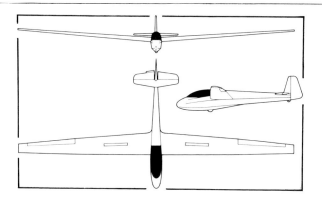

Scheibe SF-25C and C-S Falke '79 / West Germany

The Scheibe SF-25C is an improved version of the side-by-side two-seat SF-25B powered sailplane, to which it is structurally similar. The primary difference lies in the use of a more powerful engine, giving improved performance. By August 1979 a total of 285 SF-25C Falkes had been built by Scheibe, with a further 50 being built by Sportavia. Current models, known as the Falke '79, incorporate a number of design improvements. These include a domed canopy, enlarged fin and smaller rudder with increased sweep, a front fuselage coating of laminated glassfibre, several engine and exhaust modifications, and an optional twin-wheeled main landing gear with streamlined wheel fairings.

The two-piece wooden wings are swept forward and are joined at the centre with two bolts. Spoilers are fitted to the upper surfaces and optional wing folding is available. The powerplant is a 44.7 kW (60 hp) Limbach SL 1700 EA modified Volkswagen engine, driving a two-blade propeller. An electric starter is fitted. Fuel capacity is 45 litres (9.9 Imp gal) standard, 55 litres (12.1 Imp gal) optional.

The SF-25C Falke is built under licence in the UK by Vickers-Slingsby under the designation T.61. A version known as the Venture T.Mk 2 (T.61E) is in production for the Air Training Corps.

Data SF-25C-S Falke '79
Manufacturer Scheibe
First flight 1976
Wing span 15.25 m (50 ft 0¼ in)
Length 7.55 m (24 ft 9¼ in)
Wing area 18.2 m² (195.9 sq ft)
Wing section Mü (Scheibe)
Aspect ratio 13.8
Empty weight 375 kg (827 lb)
Max weight 610 kg (1,345 lb)
Water ballast None
Max wing loading 33.5 kg/m² (6.86 lb/sq ft)
Max level speed (powered) 97 kt (180 km/h)
Stalling speed 35 kt (65 km/h)
Min sinking speed at 40.5 kt (75 km/h) 1.0 m (3.3 ft)/sec
Best glide ratio at 37.5 kt (70 km/h) 24
Power plant Limbach SL 1700 EA, 44.7 kW (60 hp)
T-O run (approx) 180 m (591 ft)

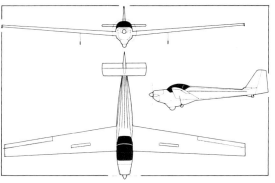

Max rate of climb at S/L 138 m (453 ft)/min
Range (45 litres fuel) 600 km (324 nm)

West Germany / **Scheibe SF-25E Super-Falke**

The Scheibe Falke series of motor gliders has proved to be one of the most popular of this class of aircraft. By the end of 1969 some 360 Falkes of types A, B and C had been built by Scheibe, 90 B and C models produced under licence by Sportavia-Putzer, and 30 had been built by Slingsby. At the First German Motor Glider Championships, in June 1970 at Burg Feuerstein, three SF-25B Falkes were among the first five.

The SF-25E Super-Falke, which first flew in June 1974, took first place in the advanced two-seater class at the First International Motor Glider Competition. It is a development of the SF-25C and features a wing increased in span by 2.7 m (8 ft 10¼ in), a feathering propeller and an adjustable engine cooling flap.

The fuselage is a fabric-covered welded steel-tube structure with a wider section aft of the wing than on the SF-25C to improve airflow at the wing root, and a larger fairing for the main landing wheel. This wheel is rubber sprung in torsion, and two outrigger wheels supported on nylon legs are fitted to the inner panels of the wing so that the outer panels can be folded for hangarage.

Data SF-25E Super-Falke
Manufacturer Scheibe
First flight 1974
Wing span 18.0 m (59 ft 0½ in)
Length 7.6 m (24 ft 11¼ in)
Wing area 17.4 m² (187.3 sq ft)
Wing section Mü (Scheibe)
Aspect ratio 17.8
Empty weight (approx) 410 kg (904 lb)
Max weight 630 kg (1,389 lb)
Water ballast None
Max wing loading 35 kg/m² (7.16 lb/sq ft)
Max speed 97 kt (180 km/h)
Stalling speed 37.5 kt (70 km/h)
Min sinking speed at 40.5 kt (75 km/h) 0.85 m (2.8 ft)/sec
Best glide ratio at 46 kt (85 km/h) 30
Power plant Limbach SL 1700, 48.5 kW (65 hp)
T-O run 150-200 m (490-655 ft)

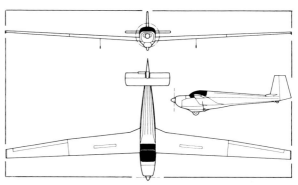

Rate of climb 144 m (472 ft)/min
Range 600 km (324 nm)

Scheibe SF-28A Tandem-Falke / West Germany

Egon Scheibe, who has more than forty years of experience in sailplane design, is currently producing the SF-28A tandem two-seat motor glider, which competed in the German Motor Glider Competition in 1977.

A distinguishing feature of the aircraft is the positioning of the cockpit above the wings, the front pilot sitting in line with the wing leading edge and the rear pilot over the main spar. It is developed from the Bergfalke and Falke and is offered as an alternative to the SF-25C and SF-25E, both of which have side-by-side seating.

The fuselage is a fabric-covered steel tube structure with a conventional wooden tail and large one-piece perspex canopy. The landing gear comprises non-retractable main wheel, outrigger wheels positioned at mid-wing on nylon legs, and a tail-wheel linked to the rudder control for manoeuvrability on the ground. The single-spar wings are constructed from wood and fabric and incorporate spoilers on the upper surface.

The power plant, situated in the nose, is a 48.5 kW (65 hp) Limbach SL 1700 EA modified Volkswagen engine driving a two-blade feathering propeller.

The Tandem-Falke is capable of very good soaring performance and in 1976 flown by Peter Ross established the two UK records for motor gliders.

Data SF-28 Tandem Falke
Manufacturer Scheibe
First flight May 1971
Wing span 16.3 m (53 ft 5¾ in)
Length 8.1 m (26 ft 6¾ in)
Height 1.55 m (5 ft 1 in)
Wing area 18.35 m² (197.5 sq ft)
Wing section Göttingen 533
Aspect ratio 14.5
Empty weight 400 kg (881 lb)
Max weight 590 kg (1,301 lb)
Water ballast None
Max wing loading 32.2 kg/m² (6.59 lb/sq ft)
Max speed 102.5 kt (190 km/h)
Stalling speed 33.5 kt (62 km/h)
Min sinking speed at 37.5 kt (70 km/h) 0.9 m (3 ft)/sec
Best glide ratio at 51 kt (95 km/h) 27
Power plant Limbach SL 1700 EA1, 48.5 kW (65 hp)

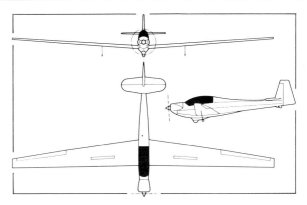

T-O run 180 m (591 ft)
Max rate of climb at S/L 126 m (413 ft)/min
Range 500 km (270 nm)

West Germany / **Scheibe SF-30 Club-Spatz**

The SF-30 is one of a long series of Scheibe sailplanes and motor gliders. It is a Standard Class sailplane built to comply with the German Club Class which was set up in an attempt to supply simple easy-to-rig robust gliders for use by inexperienced pilots. Design was started in 1973 and the prototype first flew on 20 May 1974.

Developed from the SF-27, it has a typical Scheibe welded steel tube fuselage, mostly fabric-covered. The front fuselage is glassfibre-covered and contains a large comfortable cockpit with adjustable seat and rudder pedals. Good visibility is provided by a sideways-hinged blown Plexiglas canopy.

The wings and tail surfaces are of composite glassfibre construction in that the outer surfaces of the wings are completely of glassfibre supported by plastic foam. The only concession to cheapness is in the use of spoilers in place of airbrakes. Spoilers are effective for glide-path control but are unsuitable for cloud flying. The SF-30 does not have the all-flying tail of the SF-27, but the elevators are damped and trimming is achieved by means of an adjustable spring. The landing gear consists of a non-retractable unsprung monowheel with brake, and a sprung tail skid.

Data SF-30 Club-Spatz
Manufacturer Scheibe
First flight May 1974
Wing span 15.0 m (49 ft 2½ in)
Length 6.1 m (20 ft 0 in)
Wing area 9.3 m² (100.1 sq ft)
Wing section Wortmann
Aspect ratio 24.0
Empty weight 185 kg (408 lb)
Max weight 295 kg (650 lb)
Water ballast None
Max wing loading 31.7 kg/m² (6.49 lb/sq ft)
Max speed 114 kt (211 km/h)
Stalling speed 35 kt (65 km/h)
Min sinking speed at 40.5 kt (75 km/h) 0.59 m (1.9 ft)/sec
Best glide ratio at 49 kt (91 km/h) 37

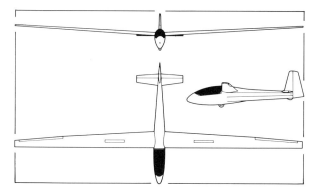

The SF-32 is the successor to the SF-27M, which won the single-seat class at the German Motor Glider competitions in 1970 and 1971. Designed in 1967, the SF-27M is similar in construction to the SF-27, but with an internally strengthened wing and control surfaces and a modified fuselage centre section. The manually-operated winding handle which raises and lowers the retractable engine has been replaced on the SF-32 by an electrical mechanism. The fuselage of the SF-32 consists of a welded steel-tube structure with the nose section covered with a moulded glassfibre shell back to the wing trailing edge. The remainder is fabric covered. The wings, which are built in two parts, are essentially those of the Neukom Elfe 17. The main spar is aluminium alloy and the covering consists of a 6 mm shell of glassfibre and plywood/foam sandwich. Schempp-Hirth airbrakes are fitted to the upper surfaces. The all-flying tailplane has a geared anti-balance tab which is also operated by the trimmer.

The power plant is a 30 kW (40 hp) Rotax 642 flat-twin two-stroke engine driving a two-blade wooden propeller. Mounted on a pylon, the engine is electrically retracted into the fuselage aft of the wing trailing edge beneath flush fitting doors.

Data SF-32
Manufacturer Scheibe
First flight May 1976
Wing span 17.0 m (55 ft 9¼ in)
Length 7.0 m (22 ft 11½ in)
Height 1.25 m (4 ft 1¼ in)
Wing area 13.3 m² (143.2 sq ft)
Wing section Wortmann FX-61-163/60-126
Aspect ratio 21.73
Empty weight 340 kg (750 lb)
Max weight 450 kg (992 lb)
Water ballast None
Max wing loading 33.8 kg/m² (6.92 lb/sq ft)
Max speed 119 kt (220 km/h)
Stalling speed 36.5 kt (68 km/h)
Min sinking speed at 43.5 kt (80 km/h) 0.65 m (2.1 ft)/sec
Best glide ratio at 48.5 kt (90 km/h) ·37
Power plant Rotax 642 2-stroke, 30 kW (40 hp)

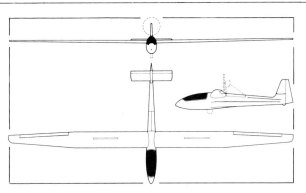

T-O run 200 m (656 ft)
Max rate of climb at S/L 120 m (394 ft)/min
Range 300 km (162 nm)

West Germany / **Scheibe SF-33**

The single-seat SF-33, new in 1977, was designed by Scheibe as a trainer motor glider to fill the gap in their range between the two-seat SF-25 series and the high-performance single-seat SF-32. It has a conventional light aircraft configuration with broad nose, and cockpit located over the wing covered by a large side-hinged blown canopy giving excellent all-round visibility.

The SF-33 is designed specifically to be easy to handle and the manufacturers have kept in mind the need for it to be used by beginners to continue their training up to a high standard of competence. The two-piece wings are constructed of wood with plywood leading edges and wooden ailerons. The fuselage is a robust steel-tube frame covered with plywood and fabric with a conventional tail unit. The landing gear consists of a fixed main wheel, a steerable tail wheel controlled by the rudder pedals and two detachable outrigger wheels which allow the pilot to operate independently of a launch crew. The gliding performance is claimed to be comparable with that of the Ka 8.

The power plant is the four-stroke BMW 900 cc motorcycle engine. Developing about 26 kW (35 hp), it drives a variable-pitch Hoffmann propeller.

Data SF-33
Manufacturer Scheibe
First flight 1977
Wing span 15.0 m (49 ft 2½ in)
Length 6.75 m (22 ft 1¾ in)
Wing area 12.5 m² (134.6 sq ft)
Wing section Scheibe
Aspect ratio 18.0
Empty weight 300 kg (661 lb)
Max weight 410 kg (904 lb)
Water ballast None
Max wing loading 32 kg/m² (6.55 lb/sq ft)
Max level speed 92 kt (170 km/h)
Stalling speed 36 kt (67 km/h)
Min sinking speed at 43 kt (80 km/h) 0.85 m (2.8 ft)/sec
Best glide ratio 28
Power plant BMW 900 cc, 26 kW (35 hp)
T-O run 150-200 m (492-656 ft)

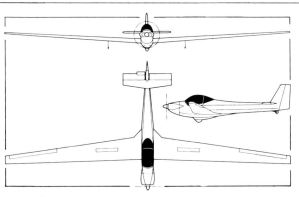

Rate of climb 150 m (492 ft)/min
Range 300 km (162 nm)

Scheibe SF-H34 / West Germany

The Scheibe SF-H34 is a two-seat glider of minimum size which can be used for ab initio and advanced training and cross-country flying. Designed by Dipl Ing Hoffmann, the SF-H34 was Scheibe's first venture into all-glassfibre construction and is designed for a long and useful life as a club trainer. The prototype first flew in October 1978 and the first production machine appeared in late summer 1979.

The glassfibre fuselage features a conventional tail unit and a large one-piece canopy, hinged to open sideways and giving excellent all-round visibility for both pupil and instructor. The cockpit incorporates semi-reclining seats with dual controls in tandem. Backrests and rudder pedals are adjustable in flight. Hooks for aerotowing and winch launching are provided.

The two-piece mid-set wing is a single-spar glassfibre structure. In the production version the wing leading edge is at right angles to the fuselage. The airbrakes are fitted to the upper surface of the wings. Easy ground handling has been assured by placing the rear of the two tandem wheels directly below the aircraft's centre of gravity.

Data SF-H34
Manufacturer Scheibe
First flight October 1978
Wing span 15.8 m (51 ft 10 in)
Length 7.5 m (24 ft 7 in)
Height 1.45 m (4 ft 9 in)
Wing area 14.8 m² (159.3 sq ft)
Wing section Wortmann FX-61-184/FX-60-126
Aspect ratio 17.0
Empty weight 290 kg (639 lb)
Max weight 490 kg (1,080 lb)
Water ballast None
Max wing loading 33.2 kg/m² (6.8 lb/sq ft)
Max speed 135 kt (250 km/h)
Stalling speed 35 kt (65 km/h)
Min sinking speed at 40 kt (75 km/h) 0.70 m (2.3 ft)/sec
Max rough air speed 86 kt (160 km/h)
Best glide ratio at 52 kt (95 km/h) 35

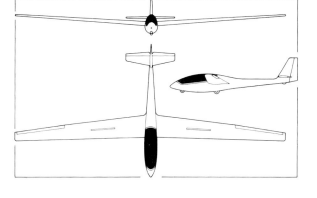

West Germany / **Schempp-Hirth Minimoa**

In 1935 two of Germany's leading glider pilots, Wolf Hirth and Martin Schempp, founded the firm of sports aircraft builders, Schempp-Hirth, in Göppingen. They designed the Göppingen 3, which they called the Minimoa (miniature Moazagotl), developing it from the 20 metre Moazagotl, and it was built by Dipl.Ing. Wolfgang Hütter and Wolf Hirth. The first Minimoa had cantilever shoulder-set gull wings. Three years were spent on its development and by 1938, with the wings re-positioned at mid-position, weight reduced and a modified aerofoil section, the Minimoa 3B was produced. From July 1935 to 1939 Schempp-Hirth built 110, thirteen being exported to France, Britain, USA, Argentina, South Africa and Japan. Several are still flying today.

The Minimoa is built from wood and fabric. Its gull wings incorporate airbrakes, and large ailerons extending from the bend to the wingtips and protruding from the trailing edges give the sailplane its characteristic shape. The cockpit, roomy for its time, is covered by a one-piece canopy (a rarity in the mid 1930s) hinged sideways. The recessed landing wheel gives a certain amount of streamlining to the fuselage. The Minimoa set many national records and for a time held the world height record of 6,687 m (21,939 ft).

Data Minimoa
Manufacturer Schempp-Hirth
First flight 1935
Wing span 17.0 m (55 ft 9¼ in)
Length 7.0 m (22 ft 11½ in)
Wing area 19.0 m² (204.5 sq ft)
Wing section Göttingen 681
Aspect ratio 15.2
Empty weight 216 kg (476 lb)
Max weight 350 kg (772 lb)
Water ballast None
Max wing loading 18.42 kg/m² (3.77 lb/sq ft)
Max speed 119 kt (220 km/h)
Stalling speed 32.5 kt (60 km/h)
Min sinking speed at 34 kt (63 km/h) 0.65 m (2.1 ft)/sec
Best glide ratio at 46 kt (85 km/h) 26

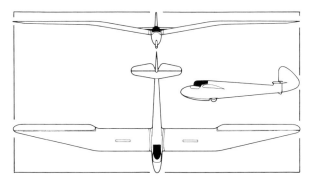

Schempp-Hirth SHK / West Germany

The SHK is a high performance Open Class sailplane which, in 1965, was the ultimate development of the wooden sailplane. It was the winner of several World and National Championships until it was outclassed by modern glassfibre aircraft. It was developed from the Austria SH, with the co-operation of the Akaflieg Darmstadt.

The most outstanding feature of the SHK is its very large V-tail, which is 50% larger than that on the Standard Austria. The wing span is also increased to 17 metres. The longer fuselage makes possible a more comfortable cockpit, which incorporates a seat easily adjustable in flight and adjustable rudder pedals.

The centre portion of the fuselage is a plywood monocoque structure with internal wood stiffening, containing the retractable landing gear and the main wing attachments. The two-piece wings have main spars of birch laminate covered with plywood and fabric. Glassfibre is used for the nose, cockpit section and tail-cone. Schempp-Hirth airbrakes are fitted and a tail brake parachute was added later. The tail unit consists of two mass-balanced all-moving tailplanes with trim tabs.

Data SHK
Manufacturer Schempp-Hirth
First flight 1965
Wing span 17.0 m (55 ft 9¼ in)
Length 6.3 m (20 ft 8 in)
Wing area 14.7 m² (158.3 sq ft)
Wing section Eppler 266
Aspect ratio 20.2
Empty weight 260 kg (573 lb)
Max weight 370 kg (816 lb)
Water ballast None
Max wing loading 25.2 kg/m² (5.16 lb/sq ft)
Max speed 108 kt (200 km/h)
Stalling speed 34 kt (63 km/h)
Min sinking speed at 37.5 kt (70 km/h) 0.6 m (2 ft)/sec
Max rough air speed 76 kt (140 km/h)
Best glide ratio at 48.5 kt (90 km/h) 38

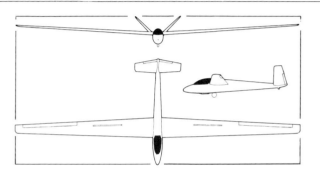

West Germany / **Schempp-Hirth Cirrus**

After thirty-two years of building sailplanes in which the stressed areas were all-wood, Schempp-Hirth introduced its first glassfibre sailplane, the Cirrus, in January 1967. It was designed and test-flown by Dipl.Ing. Klaus Holighaus.

The prototype Cirrus had an all-moving V-tail, but a conventional tail unit, with tailplane mounted part way up the fin, was adopted for all production models. Trimming is by means of spring bias in the elevator system. The cantilever wings use a thick Wortmann section and, unfashionably, do not feature flaps. Rate of descent is controlled by Schempp-Hirth aluminium airbrakes operating on both upper and lower surfaces of the wings, and

by employing the tail brake parachute. The robust flapless wing saves weight and achieves good stalling characteristics by comparison with a thinner section of similar span and aspect ratio fitted with flaps.

The construction is mainly of glassfibre/foam sandwich but with a welded steel-tube structure at the centre section of the fuselage, securing wings and landing gear attachments as well as the flying control system.

Production of the Cirrus ceased in favour of the Nimbus 2 in late 1971, but manufacture has been continued by VTC in Yugoslavia.

Data Cirrus
Manufacturer Schempp-Hirth
First flight January 1967
Wing span 17.74 m (58 ft 2½ in)
Length 7.20 m (23 ft 7¼ in)
Height 1.56 m (5 ft 0 in)
Wing area 12.6 m² (135.6 sq ft)
Wing section Wortmann FX-66-196/161
Aspect ratio 25.0
Empty weight 260 kg (573 lb)
Max weight 460 kg (1,014 lb)
Water ballast 98 kg (216 lb)
Max wing loading 36.5 kg/m² (7.47 lb/sq ft)
Max speed 119 kt (220 km/h)
Stalling speed 38.5 kt (62 km/h)
Min sinking speed at 39.5 kt (73 km/h) 0.5 m (1.6 ft)/sec
Max rough air speed 119 kt (220 km/h)
Best glide ratio at 46 kt (85 km/h) 44 .

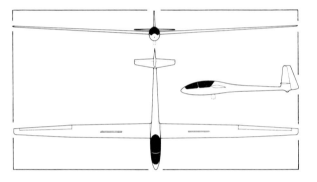

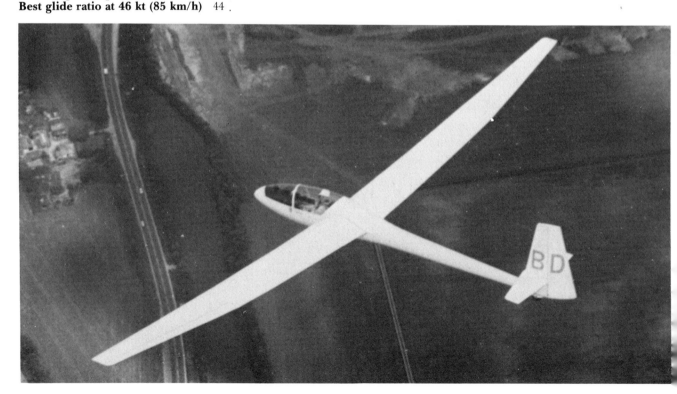

Schempp-Hirth Standard Cirrus / West Germany

The Standard Cirrus, designed by Dipl.Ing. Klaus Holighaus, flew for the first time in March 1969. It is a high performance 15 metre version of the Cirrus, but has nothing in common with it in appearance. It has a new fuselage with a T-tail and a roomy cockpit complete with a one-piece hinged canopy. The wing has a new Wortmann aerofoil but, like the Cirrus, no flaps, and the aspect ratio is reduced from 25 to 22.5, providing a good climb rate even with heavy pilots.

The large glassfibre Schempp-Hirth airbrakes operate only on the upper surface of the wings, reducing the risk of damage when landing away and keeping the lower surface of the wing aerodynamically clean. The Standard Cirrus has exceptionally docile and pleasant handling characteristics and has won national competitions all over the world.

In 1975 the Standard Cirrus, designated the '75', was improved by enlarging the fairings at the wing roots, increasing the area of the airbrakes, modifying the nose so that it is similar to that of the Nimbus 2, substituting a new type of easy-to-rig tailplane fitting and repositioning the jettison valves of the wing water tanks to a point behind the landing wheel.

Data Standard Cirrus 75
Manufacturer Schempp-Hirth
First flight Early 1975
Wing span 15.0 m (49 ft 2½ in)
Length 6.35 m (20 ft 9¾ in)
Height 1.32 m (4 ft 4¾ in)
Wing area 10.0 m² (107.7 sq ft)
Wing section Wortmann FX S-02-196 mod.
Aspect ratio 22.5
Empty weight 215 kg (474 lb)
Max weight 390 kg (860 lb)
Water ballast 80 kg (176 lb)
Max wing loading 39.0 kg/m² (7.98 lb/sq ft)
Max speed 119 kt (220 km/h)
Stalling speed 33.5 kt (62 km/h)
Min sinking speed at 40.5 kt (75 km/h) 0.6 m (2 ft)/sec
Max rough air speed 119 kt (220 km/h)
Best glide ratio at 48.5 kt (90 km/h) 38.5

West Germany / **Schempp-Hirth Nimbus 2C**

The original Nimbus single-seat sailplane was built by Klaus Holighaus in his spare time with the help of his employers, Schempp-Hirth. It has a three-piece wing of 22 m (72 ft 2¼ in) span and an aspect ratio of 30.6. The fuselage is of the Open Cirrus type. It flew for the first time in January 1969 and in the following year won the World Championship at Marfa, USA, flown by the American George Moffat.

The Nimbus 2 (photo), which currently holds two world records and has twice won the World Championships, is the production version and first flew in April 1971. It differs from the original Nimbus in several respects. The wing span has been reduced to 20.3 m (66 ft 7¼ in) and the fuselage is of the Standard Cirrus type with T-tail. The wing structure is stiffened to eliminate the bending experienced on the original Nimbus wing and is in four sections for ease of rigging and trailing. Nimbus B and C were developed in 1977 and 1978. Type B has a fixed tailplane and elevator. Type C incorporates new brake flaps instead of upper-surface airbrakes and is available either in glassfibre or in carbon fibre, the latter reducing the empty weight by 35 kg (77 lb). Together with the AS-W 17 and Jantar 2, the Nimbus 2 is generally regarded as being the highest-performance production sailplane flying today.

Data   Nimbus 2C (carbon-fibre version)
Manufacturer   Schempp-Hirth
First flight   August 1978
Wing span   20.3 m (66 ft 7¼ in)
Length   7.33 m (24 ft 0½ in)
Height   1.45 m (4 ft 9 in)
Wing area   14.4 m² (155 sq ft)
Wing section   Wortmann FX-67-K-170
Aspect ratio   28.6
Empty weight   315 kg (694 lb)
Max weight   650 kg (1,433 lb)
Water ballast   250 kg (551 lb)
Max wing loading   45.0 kg/m² (9.2 lb/sq ft)
Max speed   146 kt (270 km/h)
Stalling speed   32 kt (60 km/h)
Min sinking speed at 43 kt (80 km/h)   0.47 m (1.5 ft)/sec
Max rough air speed   146 kt (270 km/h)
Best glide ratio at 56.5 kt (105 km/h)   49

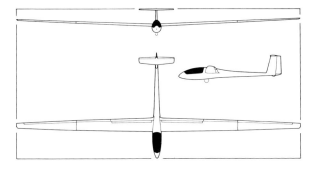

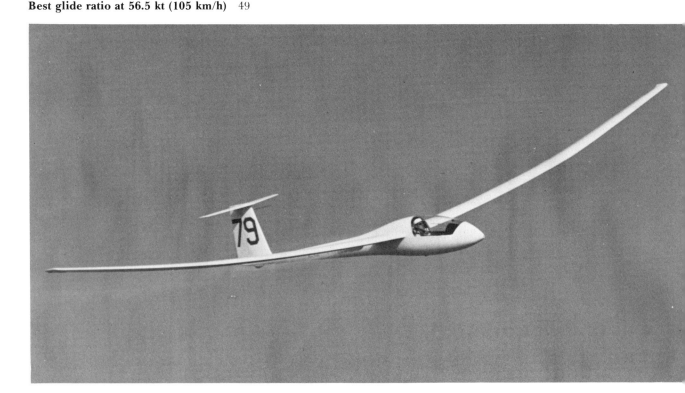

Schempp-Hirth Nimbus 2M (Motor Nimbus) / West Germany

The motor glider that attracted most interest at the First International Motor Glider Competition at Burg Feuerstein, West Germany, in June 1974 was the Schempp-Hirth Nimbus 2M, with its completely retractable 37.3 kW (50 hp) Hirth engine, which had been developed under the direction of Klaus Holighaus. The two-cylinder two-stroke engine was originally produced as a power unit for snowmobile racing in Canada.

The significance of this sailplane, like that of the 15 metre motor Cirrus (photo), lies in the fact that current top class sailplanes are now available as self-launching aircraft. In each case the weight of the engine is less than that of the water ballast carried. Raising and lowering the engine is accomplished electrically, using the motor and rack-and-pinion gearing from a Bosch car sunroof installation.

The Motor Nimbus is a mid-wing self-launching sailplane of glassfibre construction featuring four-piece wings, flaps, airbrakes, retractable landing gear, all-flying T-tail and engine mounted above the wings and retracting aft under flush doors into the fuselage. It carries 40 kg (88 lb) of fuel in its wing tanks and requires a 350 m (1,148 ft) run for take-off using the engine.

Data Nimbus 2M
Manufacturer Schempp-Hirth
First flight June 1974
Wing span 20.3 m (66 ft 7¼ in)
Length 7.33 m (24 ft 0½ in)
Height 1.45 m (4 ft 9 in)
Wing area 14.4 m² (155 sq ft)
Wing section Wortmann FX-67-K-170
Aspect ratio 28.6
Empty weight 440 kg (970 lb)
Max weight 580 kg (1,279 lb)
Water ballast None
Max wing loading 40.28 kg/m² (8.25 lb/sq ft)
Max speed 135 kt (250 km/h)
Stalling speed 37.5 kt (70 km/h)
Min sinking speed at 46 kt (85 km/h) 0.54 m (1.8 ft)/sec
Best glide ratio at 54 kt (100 km/h) 47
Power plant Hirth 0.28, 37.3 kW (50 hp)

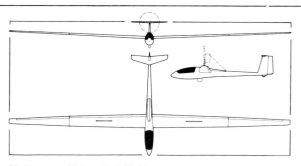

T-O run 350 m (1,148 ft)
Rate of climb 120 m (395 ft)/min
Range 500 km (269 nm)

West Germany / **Schempp-Hirth SH-7 Mini-Nimbus C**

One of the most successful of modern sailplanes is the Standard Cirrus, a development of the Cirrus. Schempp-Hirth, in a similar production pattern, has developed a 15 metre version of the Nimbus 2, designated SH-7 Mini-Nimbus. Designed by Klaus Holighaus, the Mini-Nimbus is a 15 metre Unrestricted Class sailplane, with all the features of the Open Class Nimbus 2. The prototype first flew in September 1976.

The slim glassfibre fuselage of the Mini-Nimbus, with a pointed nose similar to that of the Nimbus 2, has a one-piece flush canopy with a longitudinally-curved bottom edge for increased stiffness. The mid-set wings feature camber-changing flaps and very effective glassfibre airbrakes. The flaps, incorporating wing-root fairings, are operated by a knob in the cockpit which gives five positions between −7° and +10°, and will lower the flaps for landing, with airbrakes opening from the upper wing surface.

The trim lever is located in the same slot as the flap lever and is positioned so that when the latter is moved to lower the flaps, it operates the tailplane and gives an automatic flap/trim system.

The Mini-Nimbus B has a fixed tailplane and elevator, and the Type C is supplied either in glassfibre or with carbon-fibre wings.

Data Mini-Nimbus C (carbon fibre-winged version)
Manufacturer Schempp-Hirth
First Flight September 1976
Wing span 15.0 m (49 ft 2½ in)
Length 6.41 m (21 ft 0½ in)
Wing area 9.86 m² (106.1 sq ft)
Wing section Wortmann FX-67-K-150
Aspect ratio 23.0
Empty weight 215 kg (474 lb)
Max weight 500 kg (1,102 lb)
Water ballast 190 kg (419 lb)
Max wing loading 51.0 kg/m² (10.45 lb/sq ft)
Max speed 135 kt (250 km/h)
Stalling speed 33 kt (61 km/h)
Min sinking speed at 42 kt (78 km/h) 0.53 m (1.74 ft)/sec
Max rough air speed 135 kt (250 km/h)
Best glide ratio at 57 kt (106 km/h) 42

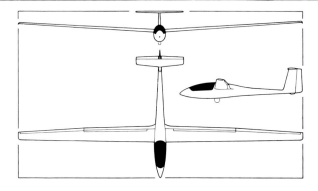

Schempp-Hirth Janus / West Germany

Although single-seat glassfibre sailplanes with flaps and tail brake parachutes have been well established for some years now, there have been few attempts to apply this material and design to the construction of two-seaters. The Janus, therefore, might well be the precursor of a new style of sailplane which could change instruction techniques of the future. Klaus Holighaus began design of the Janus in 1969 and the prototype first flew in the Spring of 1974. Production began in 1975 and 40 had been delivered by February 1977. The glassfibre monocoque fuselage is similar to that of the Nimbus 2 but the cockpit section is new. It incoporates two seats in tandem beneath a hinged one-piece canopy. The landing wheel is non-retractable and is fitted with a drum brake. There is a small nose wheel. Dual controls enable the Janus to be used for training and it is particularly suitable for cross-country instruction as it meets the requirements for a high-performance aircraft, complete with flaps and tail brake parachute. Glassfibre/foam sandwich is used for the two-piece mid-set wings, which are swept forward 2° on the leading edge. The camber-changing flaps operate between +12° and −7°. Schempp-Hirth airbrakes are fitted to the upper surfaces only.

In the 1978 version a fixed-incidence tailplane was adopted, replacing the all-moving tailplane of the earlier models.

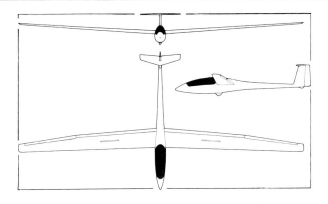

Data Janus
Manufacturer Schempp-Hirth
First flight May 1974
Wing span 18.2 m (59 ft 8½ in)
Length 8.62 m (28 ft 3¼ in)
Height 1.45 m (4 ft 9 in)
Wing area 16.6 m² (178.7 sq ft)
Wing section Wortmann FX-67-K-170/15
Aspect ratio 20.0
Empty weight 370 kg (816 lb)
Max weight 620 kg (1,367 lb)
Water ballast None
Max wing loading 37.4 kg/m² (7.66 lb/sq ft)
Max speed 119 kt (220 km/h)
Stalling speed 36 kt (67 km/h)
Min sinking speed at 40.5 kt (75 km/h) 0.61 m (2 ft)/sec
Max rough air speed 119 kt (220 km/h)
Best glide ratio at 51 kt (95 km/h) 39

West Germany / **Schleicher Condor**

Influenced by the design of the 19 m (62.3 ft) Fafnir, advised by Alexander Lippisch and supported by Dipl.Ing. Fritz Kramer, in 1931-32 the young Heini Dittmar designed the Condor. Working in his spare time he built this glider in the workshop at Wasserkuppe and entered it for the 1932 Rhön competition, which it won. It aroused general interest and later went into series production.

The Condor 1 had high-set gull wings with strengthened leading edges, braced with V-struts. The Condor 2 was developed in 1935 using a new aerofoil section, the outer part of which was thinner, improving the glide angle and rate of sink at higher speeds. This sailplane set a new world distance record of 504.2 km (272 nm) in 1935 and was the most popular glider of its time in Germany.

In February 1934 a sailplane expedition to South America resulted in Dittmar setting a new world height record of 4,350 m (14,272 ft), which until then had stood at 2,560 m (8,399 ft).

The Condor 3, built by Schleicher of Poppenhausen, came out in 1938. It featured a longer slimmer fuselage; the cantilever wings were strengthened and incorporated DFS airbrakes. After the Second World War Dittmar developed the two-seat tandem Condor 4, which has essentially the same layout as the Condor 3. It first flew in 1953.

Data Condor 3
Manufacturer Schleicher
First flight 1938
Wing span 17.24 m (56 ft 6¼ in)
Length 7.6 m (24 ft 11¼ in)
Wing area 16.2 m² (174.4 sq ft)
Wing section Göttingen 532
Aspect ratio 15.0
Empty weight 230 kg (507 lb)
Max weight 325 kg (717 lb)
Water ballast None
Max wing loading 20.06 kg/m² (4.11 lb/sq ft)
Max speed 97 kt (180 km/h)
Stalling speed 27 kt (50 km/h)
Min sinking speed 0.6 m (2 ft)/sec
Best glide ratio 28

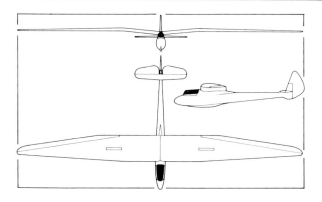

Schleicher Rhönadler / West Germany

When the Rhönadler (Rhön Eagle) first appeared in 1932, glider pilots were beginning to use thermals to make cross-country flights and were looking for a sailplane with good performance under those conditions. At that time the criterion for a successful flight had become how great a distance could be covered, rather than how long the sailplane could stay airborne. The Rhönadler was the first significant design of Hans Jacobs, who was becoming widely known through his book *Workshop Practice for Sailplane and Glider Building*.

In construction the Rhönadler shows the influence of the Fafnir, but the former is more simplified, having straight two-piece cantilever wings, tapering to the tips, and large ailerons. The conventional tail unit incorporates a large rudder and all-moving tailplane. The wide fuselage cross section permits a more roomy cockpit than had been the norm previously.

The Rhönadler was built by Schleicher in Poppenhausen and was first flown at the Rhön competition of 1932. It proved to have very satisfactory flying qualities and numerous cross-country flights were made in it over the next five years. This sailplane established Hans Jacobs as a successful designer.

Data Rhönadler
Manufacturer Schleicher
First flight 1932
Wing span 17.4 m (57 ft 1 in)
Length 7.2 m (23 ft 7½ in)
Wing area 18.0 m² (193.8 sq ft)
Wing section Göttingen 652
Aspect ratio 16.8
Empty weight 170 kg (375 lb)
Max weight 250 kg (551 lb)
Water ballast None
Max wing loading 13.89 kg/m² (2.84 lb/sq ft)
Max speed 70 kt (130 km/h)
Stalling speed 27 kt (50 km/h)
Min sinking speed 0.75 m (2.5 ft)/sec
Best glide ratio 20

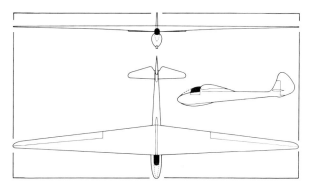

West Germany / **Schleicher Rhönbussard**

A year after the successful Rhönadler appeared, in 1933, Hans Jacobs designed the Rhönbussard for the sailplane manufacturer Schleicher. This sailplane, like its big brother the Rhönadler, has two-part cantilever wings which are attached to the top of the fuselage and contain a leading edge torsion box. It features large ailerons operated by push-rods. As on the Rhönadler the wings are secured by two conical bolts, making rigging comparatively quick and easy. The strong oval section fuselage has a short cockpit with protective windscreen. The landing gear includes a main skid and tail skid.

This little glider was regarded as a high performance aircraft in its day and pilots enjoyed flights of 200 to 300 km (108 to 160 nm) in it. Today, like many gliders of the 1930s, the Rhönbussard is valued by such organisations as the Vintage Glider Club, founded in the UK in June 1973 by Christopher Wills and Dr A.E. Slater. Members of this club have rescued restored and flown many old gliders, and at least two Rhönbussards are known to be flying in Britain today.

Data Rhönbussard
Manufacturer Schleicher
First flight 1933
Wing span 14.3 m (46 ft 11 in)
Length 5.8 m (19 ft 0¼ in)
Wing area 14.1 m² (151.8 sq ft)
Wing section Göttingen 535
Aspect ratio 14.5
Empty weight 150 kg (331 lb)
Max weight 245 kg (540 lb)
Water ballast None
Max wing loading 17.4 kg/m² (3.56 lb/sq ft)
Max speed 70 kt (130 km/h)
Stalling speed 27 kt (50 km/h)
Min sinking speed 0.75 m (2.5 ft)/sec
Best glide ratio 20

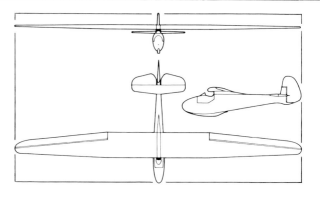

Schleicher Ka 6CR / West Germany

The successful Ka 6 series, designed by Rudolf Kaiser and developed by Rudolf Hesse, was produced as the era of plywood-built sailplanes was coming to an end. The Ka 6, which first flew in November 1956, had a wing span of only 14 m (45 ft 11 in). Later, when the regulations governing the Standard Class were published, the wing span was increased to 15 m (49 ft 2½ in) and a landing wheel replaced the skid. These sailplanes were designated Ka 6B and Ka 6BR respectively.

At the World Championships in Leszno, Poland, in 1958, Rudolf Kaiser was awarded the prize for the best Standard Class sailplane design. A Ka 6 won the Open Class and was placed third in the Standard Class; it won the Standard Class in the Championships of both 1960 and 1963 in the hands of Heinz Huth of West Germany.

Following a modification of the wing root the Ka 6C was created and, with landing wheel, the Ka 6CR. The structure is of plywood and fabric and the slightly forward-swept single-spar wings incorporate Schempp-Hirth airbrakes. Ease of rigging, high performance and reasonable price all made the Ka 6CR a very popular sailplane, and when production ceased in 1968 more than 1,400 had been built and many exported to all parts of the world.

Data Ka 6CR
Manufacturer Schleicher
First flight November 1956
Wing span 15.0 m (49 ft 2½ in)
Length 6.66 m (21 ft 10¼ in)
Wing area 12.4 m² (135.5 sq ft)
Wing section NACA 63618/63615
Aspect ratio 18.1
Empty weight 190 kg (419 lb)
Max weight 300 kg (661 lb)
Water ballast None
Max wing loading 24.2 kg/m² (4.95 lb/sq ft)
Max speed 108 kt (200 km/h)
Stalling speed 33.5 kt (62 km/h)
Min sinking speed at 36.5 kt (68 km/h) 0.69 m (2.3 ft)/sec
Max rough air speed 76 kt (140 km/h)
Best glide ratio at 43 kt (68 km/h) 29

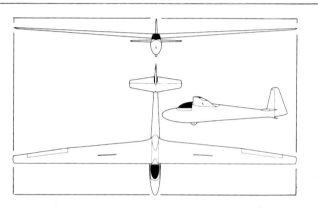

93

West Germany / **Schleicher Ka 6E**

The Ka 6E, produced concurrently with the Ka 6CR for about three years, has proved to be one of the most popular Standard Class sailplanes and has numerous national championships to its credit. It is a development of both the Ka 6CR and the Ka 10. The latter was a modified Ka 6CR with an all-moving tailplane positioned about a third of the way up the fin. However, this version never reached full production although one took part in the 1965 World Championships at South Cerney.

The Ka 6E wing is basically the same as that of the Ka 6CR but has a modified leading edge profile. Schempp-Hirth airbrakes are incorporated. The tailplane is the same as that on the Ka 10, being all-moving, but without tabs. Stability and trimming are provided by a single lever which adjusts the spring tension on the control column. The wood semi-monocoque fuselage has a different profile from the Ka 6CR, the cross section area being reduced by 10%. The cockpit has been enlarged by elongating the canopy and nose, while the canopy itself is lowered by three inches. The wing is mounted lower on the fuselage, and these improvements have resulted in better penetration.

Data   Ka 6E
Manufacturer   Schleicher
First flight   Spring 1965
Wing span   15.0 m (49 ft 2½ in)
Length   6.66 m (21 ft 10¼ in)
Height   1.6 m (5 ft 3 in)
Wing area   12.4 m² (135.5 sq ft)
Wing section   NACA 63618/63615/Joukowsky 12%
Aspect ratio   18.1
Empty weight   190 kg (419 lb)
Max weight   300 kg (661 lb)
Water ballast   None
Max wing loading   24.2 kg/m² (4.95 lb/sq ft)
Max speed   108 kt (200 km/h)
Stalling speed   32 kt (59 km/h)
Min sinking speed at 38 kt (70 km/h)   0.65 m (2.1 ft)/sec
Max rough air speed   54 kt (100 km/h)
Best glide ratio at 43 kt (80 km/h)   34

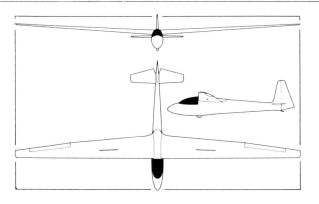

Schleicher Ka 7 / West Germany

Rudolf Kaiser, designer of the Ka 7, realised a boyhood dream when, as a young man, he built his first glider, the 10-metre Ka 1, and later flew it to gain his Silver 'C' badge. In 1952 he joined Alexander Schleicher at Poppenhausen and designed the wooden two-seat Ka 2 and its development, the Ka 2B, which became a very popular trainer in Germany.

The aim of the Ka 7 design was to produce a two-seat sailplane which would not only provide basic training but would enable pilots to continue without a break their training for flying the high performance sailplanes of that time.

The Ka 7 is a tandem two-seat aircraft with cantilever high swept-forward single-spar wooden wing incorporating plywood-covered leading edge torsion box and Schempp-Hirth airbrakes fitted above and below each wing. The fuselage consists of a fabric-covered steel tube frame similar to that of the Ka 4.

The Ka 2B had set German height records in 1959 and the Ka 7 twice improved on German distance records, and more than ten years after its first appearance set a new German goal flight record for two-seat sailplanes. The Ka 7 was always a popular club glider and is still flying in several clubs today.

Data Ka 7
Manufacturer Schleicher
First flight 1959
Wing span 16.0 m (52 ft 5¾ in)
Length 8.1 m (26 ft 6¾ in)
Wing area 17.5 m² (188.4 sq ft)
Wing section Göttingen 535/549
Aspect ratio 14.6
Empty weight 280 kg (617 lb)
Max weight 480 kg (1,058 lb)
Water ballast None
Max wing loading 27.43 kg/m² (5.62 lb/sq ft)
Max speed 108 kt (200 km/h)
Stalling speed 32 kt (60 km/h)
Min sinking speed at 38 kt (70 km/h) 0.85 m (2.8 ft)/sec
Max rough air speed 70 kt (130 km/h)
Best glide ratio at 43 kt (80 km/h) 26

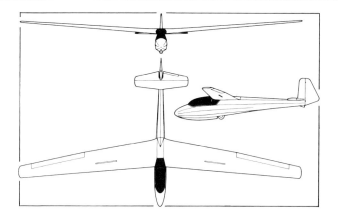

West Germany / **Schleicher Ka 8B**

Designed by Rudolf Kaiser, the Ka 8B is a single-seat trainer version of the Ka 7 two-seater. It is derived from the Ka 6 but the structure is similar to that of the Ka 7 and is suitable for amateur construction. It has good flying characteristics and is useful in weak thermal conditions, making it ideal for club use.

The Ka 8 is robust, having a welded steel-tube fuselage structure with spruce longerons covered with fabric, and a glassfibre nose cone. A fixed landing wheel with brake is fitted, together with a skid at the nose and a steel spur at the tail. The wings are of single-spar construction with plywood D leading edge and are fabric covered aft of the spar. The Schempp-Hirth airbrakes are fitted on both upper and lower surfaces of the wings. The tail unit is of wooden construction, plywood covered, and the control surfaces are fabric-covered. Since the prototype first flew in 1957 there have been three versions of the canopy; the original models were fitted with a very small canopy, the second incorporated windows on the sides of the cockpit to admit more light, and the third, on the Ka 8B, is larger.

More than 1,100 Ka 8s of all versions have been built.

Data Ka 8B
Manufacturer Schleicher
First flight November 1957
Wing span 15.0 m (49 ft 2½ in)
Length 7.0 m (22 ft 11½ in)
Height 1.57 m (5 ft 1¾ in)
Wing area 14.15 m² (152.3 sq ft)
Wing section Göttingen 533/532
Aspect ratio 15.9
Empty weight 190 kg (419 lb)
Max weight 310 kg (683 lb)
Water ballast None
Max wing loading 21.9 kg/m² (4.48 lb/sq ft)
Max speed 108 kt (200 km/h)
Stalling speed 29 kt (54 km/h)
Min sinking speed at 32.5 kt (60 km/h) 0.65 m (2.1 ft)/sec
Max rough air speed 70 kt (130 km/h)
Best glide ratio at 39.5 kt (73 km/h) 27

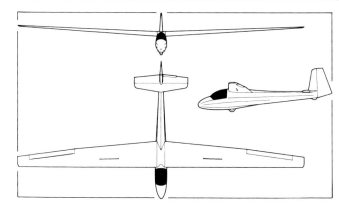

Schleicher AS-W 12 / West Germany

The Schleicher AS-W 12 is the production version of the famous D-36 Circe from Akaflieg Darmstadt, which won the 1964 German Nationals. Designed by Gerhard Waibel it is generally conceded to be one of the highest performance production sailplanes in the world. The prototype was first flown on 31 December 1965 by Edgar Krämer, its builder, and since then pilots have achieved many significant flights in it.

Constructed of glassfibre/balsa sandwich, it features long thin wings, full-span camber-changing flaps coupled with ailerons, a long slender fuselage, fully reclining seat, large retractable landing wheel and a T tail. It can be intimidating to handle because it relies solely on an unjettisonable tail parachute for glide-path control when landing and therefore presents a challenge to aspiring competition-minded pilots. In 1969, W. Scott of the USA set a new world goal flight record of 966 km (520 nm), and in 1970, H.W. Grosse of West Germany joined the small group of pilots to achieve 1,000 km (540 nm) flights. A few weeks later he was runner-up in the World Championships in Texas, where five of the first nine Open Class winners from USA, France, West Germany and the UK were flying the AS-W 12. In 1972 Grosse set a world distance record of 1,460.8 km (788 nm) which still stood in late 1977.

Data AS-W 12
Manufacturer Schleicher
First flight December 1965
Wing span 18.3 m (60 ft 0½ in)
Length 7.35 m (24 ft 1½ in)
Wing area 13.0 m² (140 sq ft)
Wing section Wortmann FX-62-K-131 mod.
Aspect ratio 25.8
Empty weight 295 kg (650 lb)
Max weight 430 kg (948 lb)
Water ballast None
Max wing loading 32.0 kg/m² (6.57 lb/sq ft)
Max speed 108 kt (200 km/h)
Stalling speed 35 kt (65 km/h)
Min sinking speed at 39 kt (72 km/h) 0.49 m (1.6 ft)/sec
Max rough air speed 54 kt (100 km/h)
Best glide ratio at 51 kt (95 km/h) 47

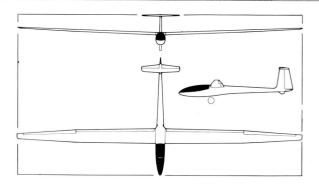

West Germany / **Schleicher AS-K 13**

In 1965 Rudolf Kaiser continued development of the two-seat Ka 2 and Ka 7, and by introducing many improvements produced the AS-K 13. It is built by Schleicher of mixed materials, including metal, wood and glassfibre. The swept-forward single-spar wings, retaining the basic constructional principles of the Ka 7 design, are repositioned from upper to mid position, allowing space for a large blown side-hinged canopy and making possible a good all-round view for both pilots. Seating comfort is improved by using glassfibre, and a sprung landing wheel is incorporated for a softer touchdown.

The fabric-covered steel-tube frame fuselage has its upper side lined with a plywood shell and the nose is glassfibre. The wings are of plywood, fabric covered and have 6° forward sweep and 5° dihedral. Metal Schempp-Hirth airbrakes are fitted and the ailerons are of diagonally-laid fabric-covered plywood. A Flettner trim tab is built into the elevator. Push-rods are used for aileron and elevator controls, with cables for the rudder.

The prototype first flew in July 1966 and some 750 have been completed to date, with production continuing.

Data AS-K 13
Manufacturer Schleicher
First flight July 1966
Wing span 16.0 m (52 ft 5¾ in)
Length 8.18 m (26 ft 10 in)
Height 1.6 m (5 ft 3 in)
Wing area 17.5 m² (188.4 sq ft)
Wing section Göttingen 535/549
Aspect ratio 14.6
Empty weight 290 kg (639 lb)
Max weight 480 kg (1,058 lb)
Water ballast None
Max wing loading (2-seater) 27.4 kg/m² (5.61 lb/sq ft)
Max speed 108 kt (200 km/h)
Stalling speed 33 kt (61 km/h)
Min sinking speed at 35 kt (64 km/h) 0.81 m (2.7 ft)/sec
Max rough air speed 76 kt (140 km/h)
Best glide ratio at 48.5 kt (90 km/h) 28

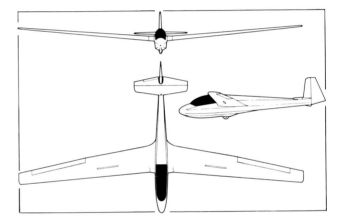

Schleicher AS-K 14 / West Germany

To avoid confusion with the well-known AS-W 12, which Schleicher also built, the Ka 12 motor glider was renamed the AS-K 14. It is a single-seat motor glider using a Ka 6E fuselage with the wings repositioned, lowering the wing root, and with the addition of a tall retractable landing wheel, designed to give the propeller adequate ground clearance. The prototype first flew on 25 April 1967.

The cantilever wing is a single-spar wood and fabric structure featuring plywood-covered ailerons, and spoilers on the upper surfaces. The cockpit is covered by a one-piece Plexiglas canopy which gives excellent visibility and is hinged to starboard. The fuselage is of conventional semi-monocoque wood and plywood construction. The 26 hp four cylinder two-stroke Hirth engine, started manually, drives a two-blade feathering Hoffmann propeller and is sited conventionally in the nose.

In the first German motor glider competition, held in 1970, AS-K 14s took second, third and fourth places, and six years later at the sixth German motor glider competition the still popular AS-K 14s took second and third places.

One AS-K 14 has been fitted with an experimental turbojet of 90 kg thrust. The exhaust is routed through the wings and out through slots at the wing tips.

Data AS-K 14
Manufacturer Schleicher
First flight April 1967
Wing span 14.3 m (46 ft 11 in)
Length 6.6 m (21 ft 7¾ in)
Height 1.6 m (5 ft 3 in)
Wing area 12.68 m² (136.5 sq ft)
Wing section NACA 63-618/615
Aspect ratio 16.8
Empty weight 245 kg (540 lb)
Max weight 360 kg (794 lb)
Water ballast None
Max wing loading 28.6 kg/m² (5.85 lb/sq ft)
Max speed 108 kt (200 km/h)
Stalling speed 33.5 kt (62 km/h)
Min sinking speed at 39 kt (72 km/h) 0.75 m (2.5 ft)/sec
Best glide ratio at 44.5 kt (83 km/h) 28
Power plant Hirth F10 K19 2-stroke, 19.4 kW (26 hp)

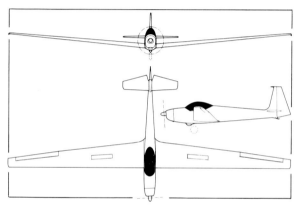

T-O run 120 m (394 ft)
Rate of climb 150 m (492 ft)/min

West Germany / **Schleicher AS-W 15**

In the summer of 1968, Schleicher at Poppenhausen brought out the high performance single-seat Standard Class AS-W 15. The W in the type designation is a credit for the young designer Dipl.Ing. Gerhard Waibel, who had previously designed the D-36 Circe at Akaflieg Darmstadt, and the AS-W 12.

The AS-W 15 is built from glassfibre, of conventional shape and beautifully streamlined. The wings and fuselage are of glassfibre/foam sandwich structure. Easy rigging is achieved by the use of tongue-fork connections for the wings, secured by two bolts. When the AS-W 15 first appeared it featured a fixed wheel and fairing which could be converted to retractable landing gear for Open Class competitions, but with the relaxing of this requirement the retractable wheel has become standard equipment. The cockpit is large with semi-reclining seat and in-flight adjustable rudder pedals. The Schempp-Hirth airbrakes are spring-sealed to preserve the streamlining.

A number of improvements are incorporated in the AS-W 15B. They include a larger landing wheel, strengthened keel, longer cockpit, larger rudder and increased all-up weight. The bearings in the wing have been replaced by ball bearings, and two 40-litre water tanks are optional extras.

Data AS-W 15
Manufacturer Schleicher
First flight April 1968
Wing span 15.0 m (49 ft 2¼ in)
Length 6.48 m (21 ft 3 in)
Height 1.45 m (4 ft 9 in)
Wing area 11.0 m² (118.4 sq ft)
Wing section Wortmann FX-61-163/FX-60-126
Aspect ratio 20.45
Empty weight 230 kg (507 lb)
Max weight 408 kg (899 lb)
Water ballast 90 kg (198 lb)
Max wing loading 37.1 kg/m² (7.59 lb/sq ft)
Max speed 119 kt (220 km/h)
Stalling speed 34 kt (63 km/h)
Min sinking speed at 39.5 kt (73 km/h) 0.59 m (1.9 ft)/sec
Max rough air speed 119 kt (220 km/h)
Best glide ratio at 48.5 kt (90 km/h) 38

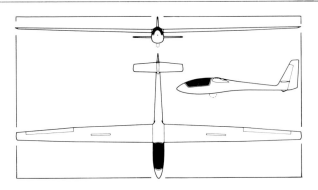

Schleicher AS-K 16 / West Germany

The AS-K 16 two-seat motor glider is a large aircraft which looks more like a conventional light plane than a motor glider. With its side-by-side seating and dual controls it is suitable for use as a training sailplane.

Construction began in 1970 and the prototype first flew on 2 February 1971, making its first public appearance at the second motor glider contest at Burg Feuerstein in June 1971, although it didn't compete. It is no longer in production.

The AS-K 16 is of mixed construction with a welded steel-tube frame fuselage with glassfibre, plywood and fabric covering. It has a one-piece side-opening blown canopy. The tailplane is a fabric-covered wooden structure utilising combined trim and anti-balance tabs on the elevator. The low-set single-spar wings are of fabric covered wood with glassfibre tips. The landing gear comprises inward retracting main wheels and a non-retractable tailwheel, and uses rubber shock absorbers and Tost drum brakes. The aircraft is powered by a 53.7 kW (72 hp) Limbach SL 1700 EB1 (modified Volkswagen) engine driving a Hoffmann HO-V62 two-blade variable pitch propeller.

An AS-K 16, flown by Hans Werner Grosse and R. Kaiser, was placed third in the First International Motor Glider Competition in 1974.

Data AS-K 16
Manufacturer Schleicher
First flight February 1971
Wing span 16.0 m (52 ft 5¾ in)
Length 7.32 m (24 ft 0¼ in)
Height 2.10 m (6 ft 10¾ in)
Wing area 19.0 m² (204.5 sq ft)
Wing section NACA 63618/Joukowsky 12%
Aspect ratio 13.5
Empty weight 470 kg (1,036 lb)
Max weight 700 kg (1,543 lb)
Water ballast None
Max wing loading 37.0 kg/m² (7.57 lb/sq ft)
Max speed 108 kt (200 km/h)
Stalling speed 37 kt (69 km/h)
Min sinking speed at 40 kt (74 km/h) 1.0 m (3.3 ft)/sec
Best glide ratio at 51 kt (94 km/h) 25
Power Plant Limbach SL 1700 EB1, 53.7 kW (72 hp)

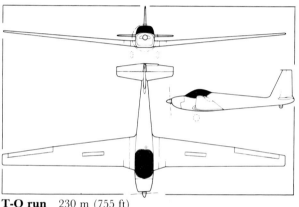

T-O run 230 m (755 ft)
Rate of climb at S/L 150 m (492 ft)/min
Range 500 km (270 nm)

West Germany / **Schleicher AS-W 17**

The AS-W 17, designed by Gerhard Waibel, is a single-seat Open Class sailplane designed with the experience gained from the AS-W 12. The prototype first flew on 17 July 1971 and fifty-two of the type had been built by January 1977. Unlike the AS-W 12's very thin wing the AS-W 17 has a thick modified Wortmann section which enables it to hold up to 100 kg (220 lb) of water ballast, and is fitted with large Schempp-Hirth aluminium airbrakes on both upper and lower wing surfaces. The camber-changing flaps are integrated with the aileron system. The wing is in four pieces, making rigging and trailing easier. The fuselage consists of a two-skin glassfibre sandwich of a special plastic hexcell monocoque structure. It features shock-absorbing retractable landing gear and a conventional tail unit. Several world records have been set in AS-W 17s, including a goal flight of 1,231.8 km (655 nm) by W. Grosse of Germany in 1974. An AS-W 17 took second place in the 1972 World Championships at Vrsac, third place at Waikerie in 1974, and first place in Finland in 1976 and in France in 1978. The AS-W 17 is generally considered to be the highest performance sailplane currently in production.

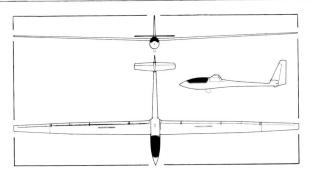

Data   AS-W 17
Manufacturer   Schleicher
First flight   July 1971
Wing span   20.0 m (65 ft 7½ in)
Length   7.55 m (24 ft 9¼ in)
Height   1.86 m (6 ft 1¼ in)
Wing area   14.84 m² (159.8 sq ft)
Wing section   Wortmann FX-62-K-131 (modified)
Aspect ratio   27
Empty weight   405 kg (893 lb)
Max weight   570 kg (1,257 lb)
Water ballast   100 kg (220 lb)
Max wing loading   38.4 kg/m² (7.86 lb/sq ft)
Max speed   129 kt (240 km/h)
Stalling speed   36.5 kt (68 km/h)
Min sinking speed at 40.5 kt (75 km/h)   0.5 m (1.6 ft)/sec
Max rough air speed   129 kt (240 km/h)
Best glide ratio at 56.5 kt (105 km/h)   48.5

Schleicher AS-K 18 / West Germany

The AS-K 18, which first flew in October 1974, is a single-seat Club Class sailplane based on the design of the Ka 6E and Ka 8. It combines the simple, rugged construction, docile flying characteristics and ability to soar in weak thermals of the Ka 8 with the cross-country performance of the Ka 6E. The AS-K 18 is designed to progress pilots from first solos to early competition flying. The fuselage consists of a welded steel-tube frame with spruce longerons covered with fabric, with a glassfibre nose section. The cockpit, with its hinged blown Plexiglas canopy, provides excellent visibility and good seating arrangement with plenty of leg room. The aircraft has no front skid as the fixed landing wheel is located just ahead of the centre of gravity. It incorporates an internal brake and a sprung tail skid is provided. The wing uses the same aerofoil section as the Ka 6E and is of single-spar wooden construction with Schempp-Hirth airbrakes operating on both upper and lower surfaces. The ailerons are plywood covered and the wing trailing edges fabric covered. The tail unit is conventional in configuration, constructed of plywood skin with fabric covered control surfaces and Flettner trim tabs on the elevator.

Data AS-K 18
Manufacturer Schleicher
First flight October 1974
Wing span 16.0 m (52 ft 5¾ in)
Length 7.0 m (22 ft 11½ in)
Height 1.68 m (5 ft 6 in)
Wing area 12.99 m² (139.8 sq ft)
Wing section NACA 63618/Joukowsky 12%
Aspect ratio 19.7
Empty weight 215 kg (474 lb)
Max weight 335 kg (739 lb)
Water ballast None
Max wing loading 23.0 kg/m² (4.71 lb/sq ft)
Max speed 108 kt (200 km/h)
Stalling speed 32.5 kt (60 km/h)
Min sinking speed at 35 kt (65 km/h) 0.6 m (2 ft)/sec.
Max rough air speed 108 kt (200 km/h)
Best glide ratio at 40.5 kt (75 km/h) 34

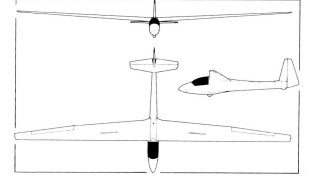

West Germany / **Schleicher AS-W 19**

Even though the AS-W 15 continues to be popular, Schleicher decided to produce a sailplane of similar configuration for more competitive pilots. The AS-W 19 benefits from the new Standard Class and 15 m Unrestricted Class rules (1975), which permit camber-changing flaps and water ballast.

Designed by Gerhard Waible, himself a competition pilot, the AS-W 19 is a single-seat Standard Class sailplane with no flaps, while the AS-W 20 is a 15 m Unrestricted Class version.

The wing is almost identical to that of the AS-W 15, except for the lower aspect ratio and thinner profile, and is strengthened to accommodate more water ballast. The fuselage was completely redesigned, resulting in a slimmer outline, and the nose profile is similar to that of the AS-W 17. Of glassfibre/honeycomb sandwich construction, the fuselage has a large and roomy cockpit. Unlike the AS-W 15, the 19 has a T-tail with fixed-incidence tailplane and elevator. Landing gear consists of a manually retractable monowheel with disc brake, and a tail skid.

With its easy, docile handling, the AS-W 19 has proved a very successful sailplane, winning several national championships and the Standard Class World Championship at Chateauroux in France in 1978.

Data   AS-W 19
Manufacturer   Schleicher
First flight   November 1975
Wing span   15.0 m (49 ft 2½ in)
Length   6.8 m (22 ft 4 in)
Height   1.42 m (4 ft 8 in)
Wing area   11.0 m² (118.4 sq ft)
Wing section   Wortmann FX-61-163/60-126
Aspect ratio   20.4
Empty weight   245 kg (540 lb)
Max weight   454 kg (1,000 lb)
Water ballast   100 kg (220 lb)
Max wing loading   41.27 kg/m² (8.4 lb/sq ft)
Max speed   138 kt (255 km/h)
Stalling speed   36 kt (67 km/h)
Min sinking speed at 39 kt (72 km/h)   0.70 m (2.3 ft)/sec
Max rough air speed   132 kt (245 km/h)
Best glide ratio at 60 kt (110 km/h)   38.5

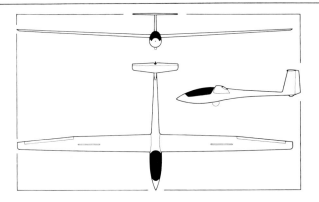

Schleicher AS-W 20 / West Germany

The Schleicher AS-W 20 is a single-seat 15 m Unrestricted Class version of the AS-W 19. Both aircraft are generally similar but the AS-W 20 features camber-changing flaps, longer, narrower ailerons, and larger upper-surface airbrakes. The emphasis in performance is on high speed, making the AS-W 20 eminently suitable for competition. The AS-W 20 prototype first flew in January 1977, 14 months after the AS-W 19. The cockpit layout and forward-hinged canopy are identical to those of the AS-W 19, except for an additional lever on the left-hand side of the cockpit to operate the flaps. The flaps move in harmony with the ailerons, though the latter rise to −8° when the flaps are lowered from +15° to +55° for landing. This also provides good roll control at low speeds. The AS-W 20 has numerous championships to its credit and is proving to be one of the most popular 15 m sailplanes. Summer 1978 saw the introduction of the AS-W 20L, featuring detachable wingtips fitted with ailerons. These changes converted it into an Open Class 16.5 m (54 ft 3 in) sailplane and increased the performance to include a best glide ratio of 45 and a minimum sink rate of 0.55 m (1.8 ft)/sec.

Data AS-W 20
Manufacturer Schleicher
First flight January 1977
Wing span 15.0 m (49 ft 2½ in)
Length 6.82 m (22 ft 4½ in)
Height 1.45 m (4 ft 9 in)
Wing area 10.5 m² (113.0 sq ft)
Wing section Wortmann FX-62K-131
Aspect ratio 21.43
Empty weight 250 kg (551 lb)
Max weight 454 kg (1,000 lb)
Water ballast 120 kg (265 lb)
Max wing loading 43.2 kg/m² (8.85 lb/sq ft)
Max speed 146 kt (270 km/h)
Stalling speed 35.5 kt (65 km/h)
Max rough air speed 97 kt (180 km/h)
Min sinking speed at 39 kt (73 km/h) 0.60 m (1.97 ft)/sec
Best glide ratio at 54 kt (100 km/h) 43

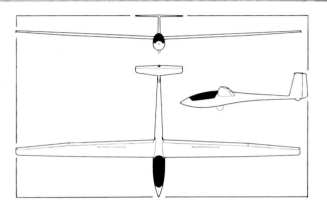

West Germany / **Schleicher AS-K 21**

The AS-K 21, designed by Ing. R. Kaiser, was developed as a successor to the popular AS-K 13 to meet a requirement for a modern two-seater of reasonable cost which would bridge the gap between training gliders and high-performance single-seat sailplanes. The AS-K 21 is Schleicher's first all-glassfibre two-seater. It was originally planned to base the design on an improved AS-K 13 fitted with T-tail and glassfibre wings, but this approach was abandoned in favour of a completely new aircraft. The prototype first flew in December 1978 and production began in 1979.

The low, clean fuselage has two semi-reclining seats arranged in tandem under individual canopies, the front unit opening forward and the rear opening aft. Dual controls are fitted and the T-tail incorporates a fixed tailplane and elevator with spring trim. The landing gear consists of non-retractable tandem wheels – the rear of which is situated behind the centre of gravity and fitted with a drum brake – and a tail skid.

The two-piece mid-set wing is a single-spar glassfibre structure without flaps but with large upper-surface airbrakes. The tips are turned down to reduce tip stalling and to keep the wings clean when on the ground.

Data AS-K 21
Manufacturer Schleicher
First flight December 1978
Wing span 17.9 m (55 ft 9 in)
Length 8.35 m (28 ft 10 in)
Height 1.55 m (5 ft 1 in)
Wing area 17.95 m² (193.2 sq ft)
Wing section Wortmann FX-SO2-196/FX-60-126
Aspect ratio 16.1
Empty weight 350 kg (772 lb)
Max weight 570 kg (1,256 lb)
Water ballast None
Max wing loading 30.6 kg/m² (6.271 lb/sq ft)
Max speed 135 kt (250 km/h)
Stalling speed 33 kt (62 km/h)
Min sinking speed at 36 kt (67 km/h) 0.65 m (2.1 ft)/sec
Max rough air speed 94 kt (175 km/h)
Best glide ratio at 49 kt (90 km/h) 34

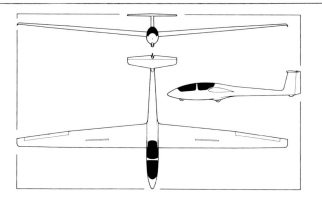

Schneider Grunau Baby / West Germany

In Germany interest in gliding was widespread by 1930; the age of the soaring sailplane was beginning and the need arose for a glider which could be used for training as well as for high performance flights. As a result, in 1931, Hirth and Schneider brought out the 12.87 m (42 ft 2½ in) span Grunau Baby, a strutted high-wing glider of wood and fabric construction with a plywood fuselage of hexagonal cross section, and open cockpit.

Two years later the Grunau workshops developed the Grunau Baby 2 with increased wing span, and later the 2a and 2b with a rectangular cross section fuselage strengthened with double layers of diagonal plywood. A windscreen protected the pilot. Schneider built about 80 Baby 1s and about 700 of the 2a and 2b versions. It was also built at other aircraft works in Europe with several thousand being built in all.

From the beginning this sailplane proved to be one of the most popular of its time and many pre-war holders of the Silver 'C' gained their certificates in a Grunau. Its success may be attributed to good stability, effective rudder action, simple construction and long span ailerons making good performance possible.

The Grunau Baby 3, built after the war, incorporated several modifications and had an enclosed cockpit.

Data Grunau Baby 2B
Manufacturer Schneider
First flight 1932
Wing span 13.57 m (44 ft 6¼ in)
Length 6.09 m (19 ft 11¾ in)
Wing area 14.2 m² (152.9 sq ft)
Wing section Göttingen 535
Aspect ratio 13.0
Empty weight 170 kg (375 lb)
Max weight 250 kg (551 lb)
Water ballast None
Max wing loading 17.68 kg/m² (3.62 lb/sq ft)
Max speed 81 kt (150 km/h)
Stalling speed 21.5 kt (40 km/h)
Min sinking speed at 30 kt (55 km/h) 0.85 m (2.8 ft)/sec
Best glide ratio at 32.5 kt (60 km/h) 17

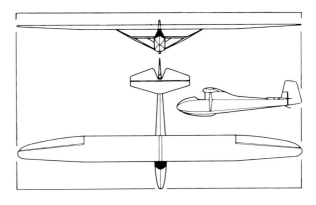

West Germany / **Schweyer Rhönsperber**

Inspired by the performance of sailplanes in thermals in the Rhön competition of 1934, Hans Jacobs developed a new aircraft in the Rhön series to take advantage of these weather conditions.

The Rhönsperber was developed from the Rhönbussard. Its gull wings were lowered, giving better visibility above and behind and the wing span was increased to 15.2 m (49 ft 10½ in). Other improvements included a larger cockpit with the instrument panel at a greater distance from the pilot than had been possible in earlier gliders, enabling him to see the whole panel at a glance. The seat and rudder pedals were adjustable and the control rods and cables were under a fixed plywood floor. For the first time spoilers were built into the wings and from these Jacobs later developed DFS airbrakes. For three years from 1935 this sailplane held undisputed rank as the leading German glider. About 100 were built by Schweyer at Ludwigshafen.

Many memorable long distance flights were made in the Rhönsperber, including two world records. In 1936, Heini Dittmar made the first sailplane flight over the Alps to Italy, and in 1937 Paul Steinig set a new world height record of 5,760 m (18,898 ft).

Data   Rhönsperber
Manufacturer   Schweyer
First flight   1935
Wing span   15.3 m (50 ft 2½ in)
Length   6.05 m (19 ft 10¼ in)
Wing area   15.1 m² (162.6 sq ft)
Wing section   Göttingen 535
Aspect ratio   15.3
Empty weight   162 kg (357 lb)
Max weight   255 kg (562 lb)
Water ballast   None
Max wing loading   16.9 kg/m² (3.46 lb/sq ft)
Max speed   108 kt (200 km/h)
Stalling speed   32.5 kt (60 km/h)
Min sinking speed   0.72 m (2.4 ft)/sec
Best glide ratio   20

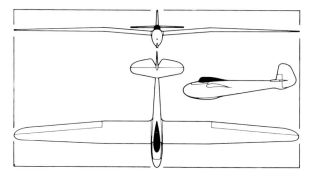

Schweyer Kranich / West Germany

The first true two-seat glider was the Dutch Fokker of 1922. In 1923 Darmstadt produced the Margarete and the Russian Niscegorodez held the two-seater distance record in 1925. But it was not until the 1930s that the real possibilities for training were exploited, and it was with the Mü 10 in 1934 and the Kranich in 1935 that the great era of two-seat dual-control training gliders was initiated.

This high-performance tandem two-seat glider was developed from the Rhönsperber. Designed at DFS by Hans Jacobs and built by Ing. Lück, the prototype was completed in the autumn of 1935; the later series aircraft were built at Schweyer in Mannheim. The Kranich, of wood and fabric construction, has mid-set gull wings fitted with spoilers, but airbrakes were fitted to the strengthened Kranich 2. The plywood fuselage has a very long narrow framed canopy with individual detachable sections. A transparent panel on each root provides downward visibility for the instructor since the rear seat is located behind the wing spar. The landing gear consists of an ash skid and a jettisonable double wheel. A total of 400 Kranichs was built in Germany and many hundreds in Sweden, Czechoslovakia, Poland, Yugoslavia and, until the late 1950s, in Spain. The Kranich held nine world and innumerable national records and in 1952 won the World Championship for two-seaters.

Data Kranich
Manufacturer Schweyer
First flight Autumn 1935
Wing span 18.0 m (59 ft 0¾ in)
Length 7.7 m (25 ft 3¼ in)
Wing area 22.7 m² (244.4 sq ft)
Wing section Göttingen 535
Aspect ratio 14.3
Empty weight 255 kg (562 lb)
Max weight 435 kg (959 lb)
Water ballast None
Max wing loading 19.16 kg/m² (3.92 lb/sq ft)
Max speed 116 kt (215 km/h)
Stalling speed 37.5 kt (70 km/h)
Min sinking speed 0.69 m (2.3 ft)/sec
Best glide ratio 23.6

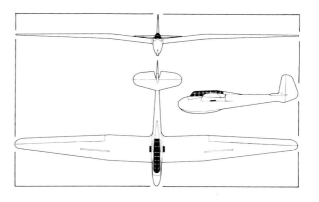

West Germany / **Sportavia RF-5B Sperber**

The Sportavia Company was formed in 1966 to take over from Alpavia the Avion-Planeur series of powered sailplanes designed by Fournier. In addition to the RF-5B, Sportavia build under licence the SF-25B and SF-25C Falke.

The RF-5B is a two-seat motor glider intended for initial training and soaring. It is an improved version of the RF-5 with the wing span increased from 13.75 m (45 ft 1¼ in) to 17.02 m (55 ft 10 in) and the rear fuselage cut down to reduce side area and improve rearward visibility from the new bulged canopy. The wing is an all-wood single-spar structure with plywood and fabric covering. The outer wings can be folded by a quick-lock system to facilitate hangarage. The

fuselage is an all-wood oval section structure of bulkheads and stringers covered with a plywood skin and the two pilots sit in tandem beneath a one-piece Plexiglas canopy hinged sideways. There is space for 5 kg (11 lb) of baggage behind the rear seat.

Powered by a 50.7 kW (68 hp) Sportavia Limbach SL 1700E Comet engine it has a choice of two types of Hoffmann propeller: a 1.45 m (57 in) diameter two-blade fixed-pitch, or a 1.5 m (59 in) diameter two-blade three-position variable pitch propeller. Fuel is carried in wing-root leading edge metal tanks with a total capacity of 38 litres (8.4 Imp gal).

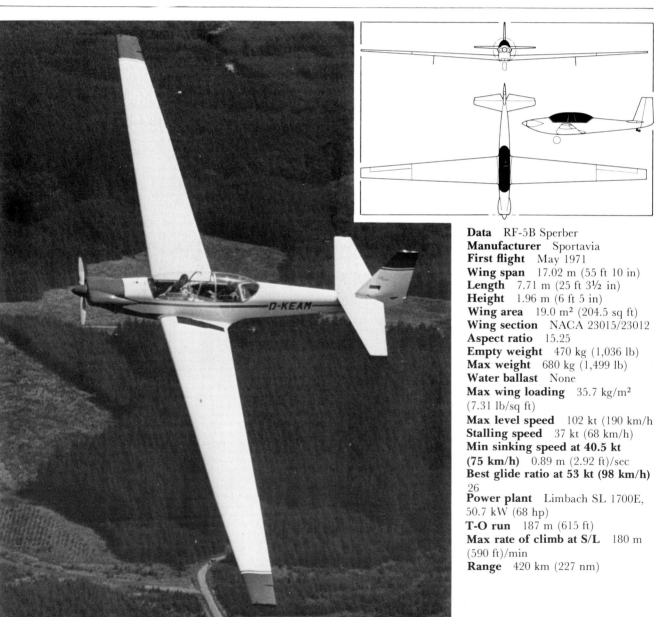

Data RF-5B Sperber
Manufacturer Sportavia
First flight May 1971
Wing span 17.02 m (55 ft 10 in)
Length 7.71 m (25 ft 3½ in)
Height 1.96 m (6 ft 5 in)
Wing area 19.0 m² (204.5 sq ft)
Wing section NACA 23015/23012
Aspect ratio 15.25
Empty weight 470 kg (1,036 lb)
Max weight 680 kg (1,499 lb)
Water ballast None
Max wing loading 35.7 kg/m²
(7.31 lb/sq ft)
Max level speed 102 kt (190 km/h)
Stalling speed 37 kt (68 km/h)
Min sinking speed at 40.5 kt
(75 km/h) 0.89 m (2.92 ft)/sec
Best glide ratio at 53 kt (98 km/h)
26
Power plant Limbach SL 1700E,
50.7 kW (68 hp)
T-O run 187 m (615 ft)
Max rate of climb at S/L 180 m
(590 ft)/min
Range 420 km (227 nm)

Start + Flug H 101 Salto / West Germany

Frau Ursula Hänle, a glider pilot herself and widow of Glasflügel's Eugen Hänle, formed a new company to manufacture the H 101 Salto. The design of this single-seat 13 metre sailplane draws extensively on that of their glassfibre sailplane, the H-30, designed by Hütter, and of the Standard Libelle. The Salto is manufactured so that several components are interchangeable with those of the Libelle.

It has a Standard Libelle wing, shortened at the root to give a 13.6 metre span, and is fitted with four flush-fitting trailing edge airbrakes hinged at their mid-point so that half the surface projects above the wing and half below. The fuselage is all-glassfibre, of robust construction and therefore suitable for club use. The aircraft features a fixed landing wheel with fairing, V-tail and a one-piece canopy which is hinged to open sideways. Although it is a small sailplane the cockpit is surprisingly roomy. The seat back is not adjustable but the rudder pedals are.

Salto is the German word for 'loop', and as its name suggests, the Salto is fully stressed for aerobatic as well as normal flying. It first flew in 1970 and by the spring of 1979 some 60 had been built.

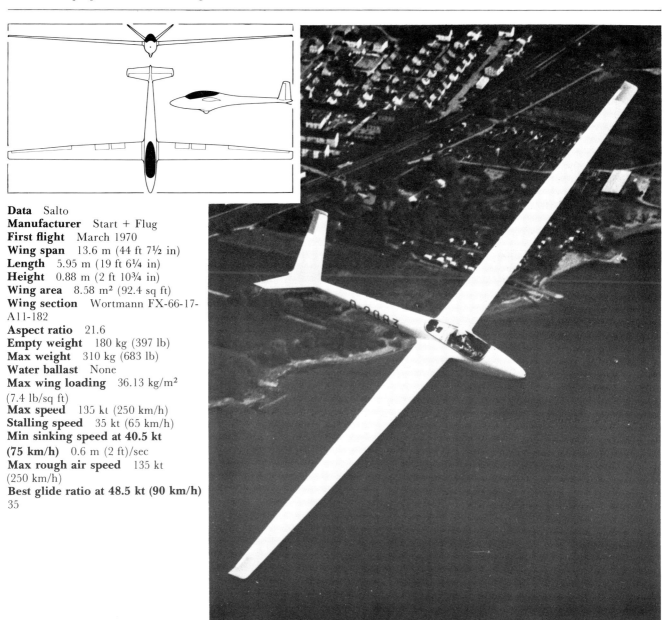

Data Salto
Manufacturer Start + Flug
First flight March 1970
Wing span 13.6 m (44 ft 7½ in)
Length 5.95 m (19 ft 6¼ in)
Height 0.88 m (2 ft 10¾ in)
Wing area 8.58 m² (92.4 sq ft)
Wing section Wortmann FX-66-17-A11-182
Aspect ratio 21.6
Empty weight 180 kg (397 lb)
Max weight 310 kg (683 lb)
Water ballast None
Max wing loading 36.13 kg/m² (7.4 lb/sq ft)
Max speed 135 kt (250 km/h)
Stalling speed 35 kt (65 km/h)
Min sinking speed at 40.5 kt (75 km/h) 0.6 m (2 ft)/sec
Max rough air speed 135 kt (250 km/h)
Best glide ratio at 48.5 kt (90 km/h) 35

West Germany / **VFW-Fokker FK-3**

The FK-3 is an Open Class single-seat high performance sailplane and is intended particularly for weak thermal conditions. Due to its ease of handling it can be flown by pilots of average ability. It was designed by Dipl.Ing. Otto Funk, and the prototype was built by apprentices at VFW (Vereinigte Flugtechnische Werke) at Speyer. The prototype first flew on 24 April 1968 and production started in January 1969.

The shoulder-set wing is built with a single metal spar with honeycomb rigid-foam supported skin with ribs of light alloy and plastic foam sandwich, spaced at 140 cm (55 in) intervals, giving the wing an extremely smooth finish.

Differential movement is embodied in the aileron and flap control circuits: the inner flaps operate to +15°, the outer flaps to +13°, while the ailerons move to +11°.

Schempp-Hirth airbrakes are fitted and water ballast is carried in two rubber tanks in the wings with the dump valve located in the fuselage aft of the retractable monowheel. The fuselage consists of a steel tube framework covered with a glassfibre shell from the nose to aft of the wing trailing edge and the narrow-diameter tail boom is of light alloy tube bolted to the framework. The tail unit is of similar construction to the wings, with a fabric-covered rudder.

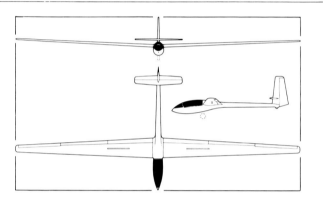

Data FK-3
Manufacturer VFW-Fokker
First flight April 1968
Wing span 17.4 m (57 ft 1 in)
Length 7.2 m (23 ft 7½ in)
Wing area 13.8 m² (148.6 sq ft)
Wing section Wortmann FX-62-K-153
Aspect ratio 22.0
Empty weight 240 kg (529 lb)
Max weight 400 kg (882 lb)
Water ballast 50 kg (110 lb)
Max wing loading 29.0 kg/m² (5.94 lb/sq ft)
Max speed 146 kt (270 km/h)
Stalling speed 27-30 kt (50-55 km/h)
Min sinking speed at 34.5 kt (64 km/h) 0.5 m (1.6 ft)/sec
Max rough air speed 146 kt (270 km/h)
Best glide ratio at 47.5 kt (88 km/h) 42

HS-2 Mrigasheer / India

The Mrigasheer is a single-seat Standard Class sailplane and is the first to be designed and developed at the Technical Centre by the team of designers and engineers led by Mr K. B. Ganesan, Director of Research and Development. The original version, the HS-1, made its first flight in November 1970. The further developed HS-2 flew for the first time in April 1973, and in the following month was placed second in the first Indian national gliding championships at Kanpur. Based on the aerodynamic design of the first HS-2, a second prototype is under construction. This has trailing-edge slotted flaps in place of airbrakes and glassfibre-reinforced plastic horizontal tail surfaces of different aerofoil section.

The wooden two-spar wings incorporate a plywood leading edge torsion box with plywood covering aft of the main spar. The rear spar carries the hinges of the wooden flaps and ailerons. The fuselage consists of a semi-monocoque wooden structure with plywood covering. The retractable unsprung monowheel is fitted with a conventional drum brake; the rubber-sprung nose-skid and rubber-sprung tailskid complete the landing gear.

Data HS-2 Mrigasheer
Manufacturer Civil Aviation Department
First flight April 1973
Wing span 15.0 m (49 ft 2½ in)
Length 7.59 m (24 ft 10¾ in)
Height 2.5 m (8 ft 2½ in)
Wing area 11.24 m² (121.0 sq ft)
Wing section Wortmann FX-61-184/163/60-126
Aspect ratio 19.85
Empty weight 237 kg (522 lb)
Max weight 335 kg (739 lb)
Water ballast None
Max wing loading 29.54 kg/m² (6.05 lb/sq ft)
Max speed 115 kt (213 km/h)
Min sinking speed 0.58 m (1.9 ft)/sec
Max rough air speed 80 kt (148 km/h)
Best glide ratio 32

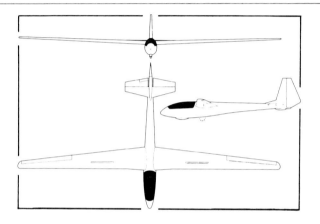

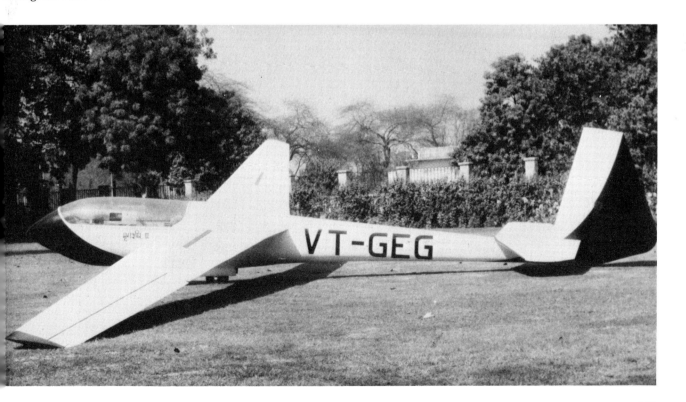

India / **KS–2 Kartik**

Though little publicised in the West, India not only has an active Government sponsored gliding movement but also designs and builds her own sailplanes and from time to time holds her own National Championships. This is a country of tremendous potential in gliding achievement with strong thermals, very high cloud bases and unexplored mountains providing excellent wave lift; but there are also great difficulties, not the least of which is the high cost of motoring. The KS–2 Kartik is a locally built single-seat high-performance sailplane developed from the KS–1 Kartik, which was designed by S. Ramamrithram. The improvements to the original design include a slight increase in fuselage length, a reduction in cockpit height and a tapered wing in place of the original 'double rectangular' wing of the KS–1. It flew for the first time on 4 May 1965, two years after the KS–1. Since then a series of these sailplanes has been built and flown and a number of improvements introduced.

The ninth Kartik model (1976) has trailing-edge slotted flaps in place of airbrakes. Construction is conventional, being of wood and fabric, although the nose cap is glassfibre. Landing gear consists of a non-retractable monowheel with drum brake and rubber-sprung nose skid with replaceable steel shoe. The tail skid is sprung with tennis balls.

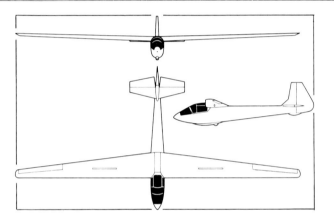

Data KS-2 Kartik
Manufacturer Civil Aviation Department
First flight May 1965
Wing span 15.0 m (49 ft 2½ in)
Length 7.37 m (24 ft 2¼ in)
Height 2.26 m (7 ft 5 in)
Wing area 13.54 m² (145.8 sq ft)
Wing section NACA 64³618
Aspect ratio 16.6
Empty weight 210 kg (463 lb)
Max weight 320 kg (705 lb)
Water ballast None
Max wing loading 23.63 kg/m² (4.84 lb/sq ft)
Max speed 108 kt (200 km/h)
Stalling speed 31 kt (58 km/h)
Min sinking speed at 35 kt (65 km/h) 0.6 m (2 ft)/sec
Max rough air speed 75.5 kt (140 km/h)
Best glide ratio at 40.5 kt (75 km/h) 31

RG-1 **Rohini** / India

A pioneer in establishing Indian gliding, Mr S. Ramamrithram, Director General of the Indian Civil Aviation Department, has designed some of the gliders himself. India's economic circumstances having precluded any significant import of foreign gliders, the majority of club aircraft have tended to be of Indian origin, and their construction to be of local materials. Indian gliders have therefore been built exclusively of wood and fabric.

The Rohini is the second two-seat glider to be designed and built in India. Designed by S. Ramamrithram, who also designed the first two seater in India, the Ashivini, four prototypes were built between 1961 and 1964 at the

Technical Centre of Civil Aviation. The first prototype flew for the first time on 10 May 1961. The Rohini uses a number of components identical to those on the Ashivini, except that the Ashivini is a tandem two-seater while the Rohini has its seating arranged side-by-side. Construction is of wood and fabric and the high-set wings are strut-braced in a similar way to those of the Slingsby T.21, to which the Rohini bears superficial resemblance.

More than 100 Rohinis have been built by Veegal Engines and Engineering Company of Calcutta, and the Hindustan Aeronautics Company at Kanpur.

Data RG-1 Rohini 1
Manufacturer Civil Aviation Department
First flight May 1961
Wing span 16.56 m (54 ft 4 in)
Length 8.17 m (26 ft 9½ in)
Height 2.33 m (7 ft 7¾ in)
Wing area 20.76 m² (223.5 sq ft)
Wing section NACA 4418/4412
Aspect ratio 13.2
Empty weight 274 kg (604 lb)
Max weight 494 kg (1,089 lb)
Water ballast None
Max wing loading 23.76 kg/m² (4.86 lb/sq ft)
Max speed 94 kt (174 km/h)
Stalling speed 26 kt (48 km/h)
Min sinking speed at 33 kt (61 km/h) 0.85 m (2.8 ft)/sec
Max rough air speed 65 kt (120 km/h)
Best glide ratio at 41.5 kt (77 km/h) 22

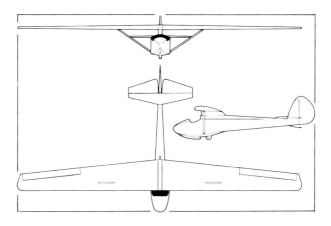

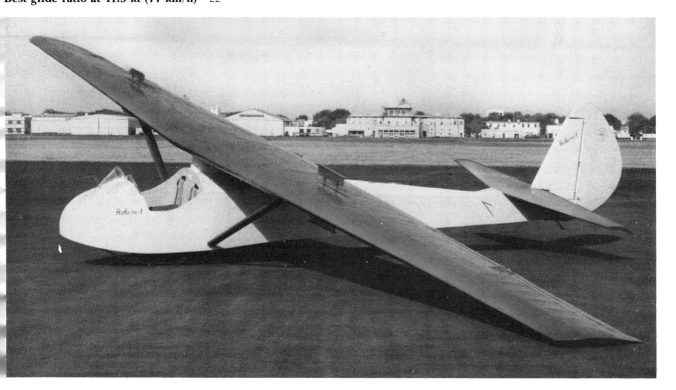

Italy / **Aer-Pegaso M-100**

Alberto and Piero Morelli designed the 14 m (45 ft 11 in) M-100 in the early 1950s, winning a competition organised by the Italian Aero Club for the best design of a single-seat sailplane. The wing span was later increased to 15 m (49 ft 2½ in) to meet the Standard class requirements. A total of about 180 was produced both in Italy by Avionautica Rio, and in France under licence by S. A. Carmam where it was known as the M-100 S Mésange (Tomtit).

This sailplane is of conventional all-wood construction, part fabric covered with beech main wing spar. The unusual airbrakes comprise three pairs of rotating plates placed above and below each wing. The cantilever all-wood tail unit incorporates elevator trim tabs and moving surfaces are fabric-covered. The cockpit contains a storage compartment for oxygen and radio equipment behind the seat and is covered by a one-piece Plexiglas canopy hinged sideways. The fuselage is an all-wood semi-monocoque structure with a single towing hook for both aero and winch launching. The landing gear consists of a rubber-sprung nose skid, non-retractable monowheel with disc brake, and a tail skid.

The M-100 first flew in 1957 and was used for a time as the standard Italian training sailplane. Stressed for normal aerobatics (but not inverted flight) the M-100 S has taken part in both national and international competitions.

Data M-100 S
Manufacturer Aer-Pegaso
First flight January 1960
Wing span 15.0 m (49 ft 2½ in)
Length 6.56 m (21 ft 6 in)
Wing area 13.1 m² (141 sq ft)
Wing section NACA 63618/615
Aspect ratio 17.1
Empty weight 198 kg (437 lb)
Max weight 315 kg (694 lb)
Water ballast None
Max wing loading 24.0 kg/m² (4.91 lb/sq ft)
Max speed 124 kt (230 km/h)
Stalling speed 27.5 kt (51 km/h)
Min sinking speed at 36 kt (67 km/h) 0.62 m (2 ft)/sec
Max rough air speed 75.5 kt (140 km/h)
Best glide ratio at 41.5 kt (77 km/h) 32

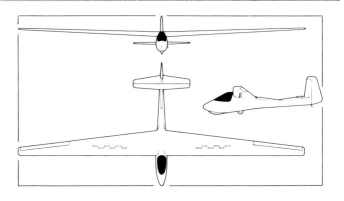

Caproni Vizzola Calif A-21S / Italy

This record-breaking two-seat high-performance sailplane, which currently holds no less than four world records for two-seaters, is built by Caproni Vizzola, the oldest Italian aircraft company. Designed by C. Ferrarin and L. Sonzio, the Calif series entered production in 1969 and the A-21 prototype made its maiden flight on 23 November 1970. The original A-21 is no longer being built, its place having been taken by the A-21S, which is described below.

The low-drag tadpole-shaped fuselage is built of glassfibre with an aluminium alloy strengthened fore section and all-metal tail boom. The all-metal fin and rudder is swept back and the all-moving tailplane is attached to the top of the fin. The roomy cockpit is fitted with dual controls and is covered by a two-piece canopy.

The cantilever mid-set wings have a rectilinear centre section and two trapezoid outer sections. A three-piece, all-metal main spar is supplemented by two auxiliary spars in the centre section and one in each of the outer panels. The wing tips are glassfibre. A special feature of this sailplane is the trailing edge flap/spoiler system, which provides camber changing surfaces between ±8° and acts as an airbrake when deflected to 89° downwards. The landing gear consists of a manually retractable two-wheel undercarriage and fixed tailwheel.

Data Calif A-21S
Manufacturer Caproni Vizzola
First flight November 1970
Wing span 20.38 m (66 ft 10½ in)
Length 7.84 m (25 ft 8½ in)
Height 1.61 m (5 ft 3½ in)
Wing area 16.19 m² (174.3 sq ft)
Wing section Wortmann FX-67-K-170/60-126
Aspect ratio 25.65
Empty weight 436 kg (961 lb)
Max weight 644 kg (1,420 lb)
Water ballast None
Max wing loading 39.8 kg/m² (8.15 lb/sq ft)
Max speed 138 kt (255 km/h)
Stalling speed 34 kt (63 km/h)
Min sinking speed at 46 kt (85 km/h) 0.6 m (2 ft)/sec
Max rough air speed 138 kt (255 km/h)
Best glide ratio at 56.5 kt (105 km/h) 43

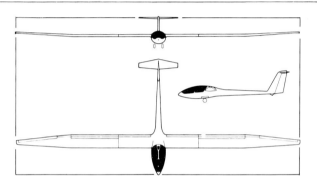

Italy / **CVT M-200**

Designed by Alberto and Piero Morelli, the M-200 is the two-seat version of the M-100. The first prototype M-200 was built at the CVT Turin, under a contract from the Aero Club of Italy, and flew for the first time in May 1964. The general layout of the M-100 is maintained, the wing and tail unit having practically the same contour, aerofoil sections and control surfaces, but of different sizes. The main feature of the M-200 is the fuselage, and the cockpit arrangement in particular. Staggered side-by-side seating is adopted; this arrangement allows good visibility for both pilots. Correct balance of the glider is maintained and there is no need for ballast when the aircraft is flown solo.

The fuselage is constructed from plywood with frames and stringers; the one-piece canopy opens sideways. The wing is derived from that of the M-100 by increasing the span from 15 m (49 ft 2½ in) to 18.15 m (59 ft 6½ in) and the aspect ratio from 17.1 to 19. The wing is a single-spar structure of wood and fabric with leading edge torsion box. The airbrakes consist of four pairs of rotating plates on each wing. The M-200 is easy to fly even for first solo and is stressed for aerobatics.

Data Morelli M-200
Manufacturer CVT
First flight May 1964
Wing span 18.15 m (59 ft 6½ in)
Length 7.6 m (24 ft 11¼ in)
Wing area 17.5 m² (188.4 sq ft)
Wing section NACA 63618/615
Aspect ratio 19.0
Empty weight 345 kg (761 lb)
Max weight 570 kg (1,257 lb)
Water ballast None
Max wing loading 32.57 kg/m² (6.67 lb/sq ft)
Max speed 121 kt (225 km/h)
Stalling speed 38 kt (70 km/h)
Min sinking speed 0.70 m (2.3 ft)/sec
Max rough air speed 81 kt (150 km/h)
Best glide ratio at 53 kt (98 km/h) 32

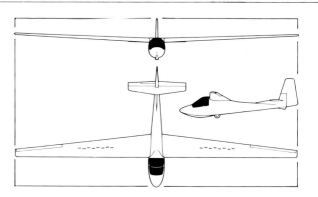

The M-300, designed by Alberto Morelli, is a single-seat high-performance sailplane of which two prototypes have so far been built and flown by the Centro di Volo a Vela at Turin. The first prototype made its first flight in April 1968. The M-300 is intended for competition and record flying, as well as for club use, and incorporates many original features. In particular careful thought has been given to constructional techniques in order to achieve the required accuracy and quality of surface finish and to reduce the time taken for construction. Some extruded structures have been introduced into the design. The wings are a composite structure with the skin being made of pre-formed thick plywood panels and the ribs milled out of a wooden sandwich. The tapered wing spar is a machined I-section beam of aluminium-zinc alloy, with lightening holes cut in the web. The wings are attached to the fuselage by Redux-bonded dural fittings.

The fuselage is a conventional semi-monocoque wooden structure, built up on four main frames and nine stringers. The nose cone is of glassfibre. The tail unit consists of a swept-back fin and rudder and one-piece narrow-chord aluminium alloy all-moving tailplane mounted on top of the fin. The rudder is double-slotted.

Data Morelli M-300
Manufacturer CVT
First flight April 1968
Wing span 15.0 m (49 ft 2½ in)
Length 6.39 m (20 ft 11½ in)
Wing area 9.16 m² (98.6 sq ft)
Aspect ratio 24.7
Empty weight 190 kg (419 lb)
Max weight 300 kg (661 lb)
Water ballast None
Max wing loading 32.7 kg/m² (6.69 lb/sq ft)
Max speed 135 kt (250 km/h)
Stalling speed 38.5 kt (71 km/h)
Min sinking speed at 42.5 kt (79 km/h) 0.62 m (2 ft)/sec
Best glide ratio at 47.5 kt (88 km/h) 38

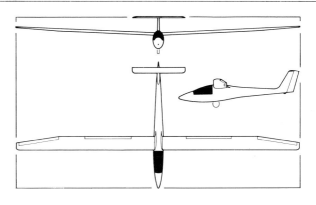

Japan / **Nippi NP-100A Albatross**

The NP-100A is a side-by-side two-seat ducted-fan motor glider. The modified 44.7 kW (60hp) Kawasaki 748 cc three-cylinder motor cycle engine, driving a four-blade wooden fan of 0.6 m (23.5 in) diameter, is situated in the centre of the fuselage under the wing root. Triple 'venetian-blind' type air intake doors, on each side of the fuselage, are interconnected with the engine starting circuit to prevent the engine from operating when the doors are closed. The 40 litre (8.8 Imp gall) fuel tank is located in the fuselage.

The fuselage is an all-metal semi-monocoque structure, with a forward-retracting twin-wheel undercarriage, operating mechanically with spring assistance. The cockpit is covered by a rearward-hinged framed canopy; dual controls are fitted. The cantilever shoulder-set wings are all-metal with two-piece flaps on each side. The inner flaps have a greater range of movement and can be lowered to 80° for use as airbrakes; the outer flaps move to 48° maximum.

Design work began in late 1973 and the prototype flew for the first time on 25 December 1975. Flight testing was carried out during 1976 as a result of which several modifications were made. The first pre-production NP-100A was expected to fly in early 1978.

Data NP-100A Albatross
Manufacturer Nippi
First flight December 1975
Wing span 18.0 m (59 ft 0½ in)
Length 8.0 m (26 ft 3 in)
Height 2.23 m (7 ft 3¾ in)
Wing area 18.0 m² (193.8 sq ft)
Wing section Wortmann FX-67-K-170
Aspect ratio 18.0
Empty weight 420 kg (926 lb)
Max weight 600 kg (1,323 lb)
Water ballast None
Max wing loading 33.3 kg/m² (6.82 lb/sq ft)
Max level speed at S/L 86 kt (160 km/h)
Stalling speed 35 kt (65 km/h)
Min sinking speed at 44.5 kt (83 km/h) 0.8 m (2.6 ft)/sec
Best glide ratio at 48.5 kt (90 km/h) 30
Power plant Kawasaki HZI 748 cc, 44.7 kW (60 hp)

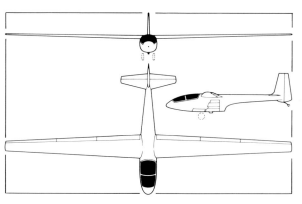

T-O run 365 m (1,198 ft)
Max rate of climb at S/L 120 m (394 ft)/min
Range 200 km (108 nm)

Although Japan competes very successfully in many of the world markets this has not included export of her sailplanes. Some single-seat high-performance sailplanes are built but Japanese teams usually fly European-built aircraft in world championships.

The Mita 3 is a popular two-seat sailplane designed and built by LADCO until that company relinquished its sailplane section to Tainan, who continued production of the Mita 3 under licence. By January 1976 thirty-seven had been built. This training sailplane features cantilever three-piece shoulder-set wings with a constant chord centre section and tapered outer panels. The wings are of all-wood box-spar monospar construction with plywood covering and fabric-covered control surfaces. Schempp-Hirth airbrakes are fitted to the upper wing surfaces. The fuselage is a fabric covered steel-tube frame with a glassfibre nose and front section. The tandem seats are covered by a flush-set two-piece canopy hinged to starboard. The wooden tail unit features a large tailplane with fabric covered control surfaces. The landing gear consists of a rubber-sprung non-retractable monowheel with brake, and a tail skid.

Data Mita 3
Manufacturer Tainan
Wing span 16.0 m (52 ft 6 in)
Length 7.96 m (26 ft 1½ in)
Height 1.28 m (4 ft 2½ in)
Wing area 15.87 m² (170.8 sq ft)
Wing section NACA 63³618
Aspect ratio 16.13
Empty weight 300 kg (661 lb)
Max weight 450 kg (992 lb)
Water ballast None
Max wing loading 28.4 kg/m² (5.81 lb/sq ft)
Max speed 103 kt (190 km/h)
Stalling speed 33.5 kt (62 km/h)
Min sinking speed at 40.5 kt (75 km/h) 0.72 m (2.4 ft)/sec
Best glide ratio at 44 kt (82 km/h) 30

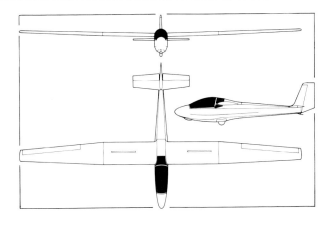

Netherlands / **Alsema Sagitta**

The Sagitta (Arrow), the first Dutch Standard Class single-seat sailplane, was designed and built by Piet Alsema after three years of planning and development. This pleasant looking sailplane features a slender all-wood fuselage with raked fin and rudder, long pointed nose and sliding blown canopy which provides excellent all-round visibility. The wood cantilever tailplane can be folded for trailing. Landing gear comprises a fixed monowheel with brake.

The two-piece mid-set wings are all-wood single-spar structures with plywood leading edge torsion box stiffening and 25% fabric covering. The ailerons are the plain wooden type and the airbrakes, which are of a special design, operate on both upper and lower wing surfaces.

The prototype Sagitta made its first flight on 4 July 1960 and the first production model, designated Sagitta 2, was rolled out on 24 November 1961. Only twenty were built, with some being exported.

The Super Sagitta, first reported in the Spring of 1964, was a project to evolve a 17 metre version of the Sagitta with increased wing and tail surface areas.

Data Alsema Sagitta
Manufacturer Vliegtuigbouw
First flight November 1961
Wing span 15.0 m (49 ft 2½ in)
Length 6.47 m (21 ft 2¾ in)
Wing area 12.0 m² (129.2 sq ft)
Wing section NACA 63³618/4412
Aspect ratio 18.7
Empty weight 217 kg (478 lb)
Max weight 320 kg (705 lb)
Water ballast None
Max wing loading 26.7 kg/m² (5.47 lb/sq ft)
Max speed 146 kt (270 km/h)
Stalling speed 35.5 kt (66 km/h)
Min sinking speed at 42 kt (78 km/h) 0.64 m (2.1 ft)/sec
Max rough air speed 108 kt (200 km/h)
Best glide ratio at 52.3 kt (97 km/h) 37

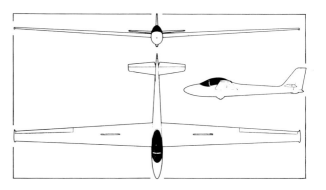

Poland's reputation as source of some of the world's finest high-performance sailplanes had been established before the war and continued in 1951 with the Jaskolka. In the six years from May 1954 to May 1960 this sailplane held no fewer than fifteen world records.

Two prototype Jaskolkas were rolled out in 1951, the first in September and the second in December. Three years of development followed before the Jaskolka entered series production. The prototype had a fuselage length of 6.74 m (22 ft 1½ in) but in the production series this was increased to 7.42 m (24 ft 4¼ in).

The two-piece cantilever mid-set wings are built of wood with fabric covering and incorporate Fowler flaps which can be lowered to 12° or 25°, and airbrakes. When the Jaskolka first appeared it incorporated many features not seen before: the moulded two-piece Plexiglas canopy with the aft section sliding back; the recessed handle built into the rear fuselage for ground handling; and the semi-retractable landing wheel.

A total of 127 Jaskolkas had been built when production ended in 1961. Many were exported.

Data Jaskolka-Z
Manufacturer SZD
First flight 1955
Wing span 16.0 m (52 ft 6 in)
Length 7.42 m (24 ft 4¼ in)
Wing area 13.6 m² (146.4 sq ft)
Wing section NACA 23012A
Aspect ratio 18.8
Empty weight 270 kg (595 lb)
Max weight 370 kg (816 lb)
Water ballast 95 kg (209 lb)
Max wing loading 27.2 kg/m² (5.57 lb/sq ft)
Max speed 135 kt (250 km/h)
Stalling speed 27 kt (50 km/h)
Min sinking speed at 40 kt (74 km/h) 0.75 m (2.5 ft)/sec
Max rough air speed 65 kt (120 km/h)
Best glide ratio at 44.5 kt (83 km/h) 28.5

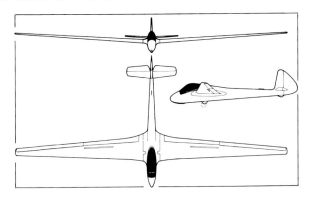

Poland / **SZD-22 Mucha Standard**

The Mucha Standard single-seat high-performance sailplane is a development of the famous IS Mucha series which dates back to 1948 and was used in great numbers by Polish gliding groups, achieving several Diamond and record-breaking flights. The SZD-12 Mucha was developed in 1957 and was the forerunner of the Mucha Standard. Designed by R. Grzywacz especially for the 1958 World Championships held in Poland, where it took first place in the Standard Class, flown by Adam Witek, the Mucha Standard has an all-wood structure. The cantilever wings have a single main spar and oblique auxiliary spar and are covered either with plywood (SZD-22B) or fabric

(SZD-22C). The fabric-covered Frise ailerons are both aerodynamically and mass balanced. Airbrakes are fitted inboard of the ailerons.

The oval section fuselage is plywood-covered and the cockpit is covered by a streamlined clamshell Plexiglas canopy. Landing gear consists of short front and rear skids sprung with rubber pads, and a monowheel. More than 240 of the type were built with many of the SZD-22C type being exported.

Two further models, D and E, were manufactured, the D type having a modified skid and landing wheel, and the E having a new wing.

Data Mucha Standard
Manufacturer SZD
First flight February 1958
Wing span 14.98 m (49 ft 1¾ in)
Length 7.0 m (22 ft 11½ in)
Wing area 12.75 m² (137.3 sq ft)
Wing section Göttingen 549
Aspect ratio 17.6
Empty weight 240 kg (529 lb)
Max weight 350 kg (772 lb)
Water ballast None
Max wing loading 25.6 kg/m² (5.24 lb/sq ft)
Max speed 135 kt (250 km/h)
Stalling speed 32 kt (59 km/h)
Min sinking speed at 38.5 kt (71 km/h) 0.73 m (2.4 ft)/sec
Max rough air speed 108 kt (200 km/h)
Best glide ratio at 40.5 kt (75 km/h) 27.8

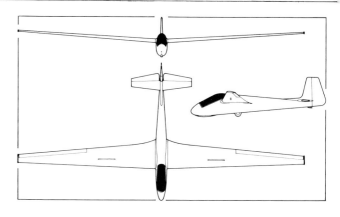

SZD-9bis Bocian 1E / Poland

One of the best known training sailplanes is the two-seat Bocian built by SZD. It is one of the few two-seat gliders stressed for aerobatics, including inverted flight. The prototype was flown for the first time on 11 March 1952 and the first production aircraft in March 1953. Several alterations were made to the tail and to the rudder in particular, and the Bocian C first flew in February 1954 followed by the D in 1958 and finally the E, which first flew on 6 December 1966. By the end of 1976 a total of 593 SZD-9 Bocians had been built.

Construction is of wood and fabric. The oval-section fuselage is plywood covered and incorporates two seats in tandem beneath a long blown Plexiglas canopy. Landing gear consists of a non-retractable monowheel with brake, and front skid. The mid-set wings are swept forward 1° 30′ at quarter chord. They consist of a two-spar wooden structure with plywood D-section leading edge and fabric covering. SZD airbrakes are fitted inboard of the slotted ailerons. Between 1955 and 1968 Polish pilots broke many world records in various models of the Bocian, including Franciszek Kepka, who set a world record goal flight of 636.6 km (344.1 nm) in 1962. The Bocian currently holds the world height records for two-seaters.

Data Bocian 1E
Manufacturer SZD
First flight December 1966
Wing span 17.8 m (58 ft 4¾ in)
Length 8.21 m (26 ft 11¼ in)
Height 1.2 m (4 ft 0¼ in)
Wing area 20.0 m² (215.3 sq ft)
Wing section NACA 43018A/43012A
Aspect ratio 15.85
Empty weight 342 kg (754 lb)
Max weight 540 kg (1,190 lb)
Water ballast None
Max wing loading 27.0 kg/m² (5.53 lb/sq ft)
Max speed 108 kt (200 km/h)
Stalling speed 32.5 kt (60 km/h)
Min sinking speed at 38.5 kt (71 km/h) 0.82 m (2.7 ft)/sec
Max rough air speed 81 kt (150 km/h)
Best glide ratio at 43 kt (80 km/h) 26

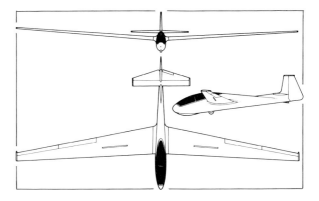

Poland / **SZD-19 Zefir 4**

The Zefir 4 was the last of the famous wood and fabric built Zefir series which resulted from work done under the leadership of Dipl.Ing. B. Szuba in Poland in 1957-8. The Open Class SZD-19X Zefir first flew in December 1958 and attracted a great deal of attention at the World Championships in Germany in 1960, where it took second and third places.

Of special interest were the slim fuselage, reclining pilot's position, slotted flaps, tail parachute, retractable wheel/tow-hook unit, and the elegant swept-back fin and rudder. The long slim canopy opens by sliding forwards about 8 cm (3 in) and then hinging upwards from the tip of the nose cone.

The Zefir 2 was rolled out in January 1961 and Polish pilots flying this type were placed first and second in the 1963 World Championships in Argentina. Efforts to raise the best glide ratio resulted in the 19 metre Zefir 3 with longer fuselage and full-span flaps. The Zefir 4, developed for the 1968 World Championships, first flew in December 1967. The tail unit had been entirely redesigned without the sweepback of previous models. The wings feature full-span Fowler flaps, the outer sections of which act as ailerons.

Data Zefir 4
Manufacturer SZD
First flight December 1967
Wing span 19.0 m (62 ft 4 in)
Length 8.0 m (26 ft 3 in)
Wing area 15.7 m² (169 sq ft)
Wing section NACA 66-215-416
Aspect ratio 23.0
Empty weight 350 kg (772 lb)
Max weight 440 kg (970 lb)
Water ballast None
Max wing loading 28.0 kg/m² (5.73 lb/sq ft)
Max speed 129 kt (240 km/h)
Stalling speed 36 kt (67 km/h)
Min sinking speed at 50 kt (92 km/h) 0.6 m (1.97 ft)/sec
Max rough air speed 108 kt (200 km/h)
Best glide ratio at 51 kt (94 km/h) 42

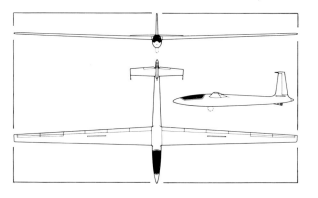

SZD-24 Foka / Poland

Designed by W. Okarmus, the SZD-24 Foka Standard Class high-performance sailplane flew for the first time on 2 May 1960. Its first public appearance at the 1960 World Championships, where it gained third place, caused a great deal of interest because of its radical new design features. Subsequently it was put into series production. Several versions were developed: the SZD-24B Foka 2, which consisted of three pre-production models only, completed early in 1961; the SZD-24C Foka Standard, which was the first major production variant and which first flew in September 1961; the SZD-24-4A Foka. The fuselage consists of a wooden monocoque structure with the front part in glassfibre. The long transparent canopy opens by sliding forward. The wings are a sparless torsion-box structure with thick plywood stressed skin. SZD metal airbrakes are fitted at 60% chord. The landing gear comprises a long nose skid and a wheel located well behind the centre of gravity.

The SZD-32A Foka 5, which first flew on 28 November 1966, won the OSTIV prize for the best Standard class sailplane design. It features a more roomy cockpit and the tailplane is repositioned to the top of the fin. By the time production ended in 1971 a total of 330 Foka series sailplanes had been built, including 200 for export to 17 countries.

Data Foka 4
Manufacturer SZD
First flight February 1962
Wing span 15.0 m (49 ft 2½ in)
Length 7.0 m (22 ft 11½ in)
Wing area 12.2 m² (131.3 sq ft)
Wing section NACA 63³618/4415
Aspect ratio 18.5
Empty weight 245 kg (540 lb)
Max weight 386 kg (851 lb)
Water ballast None
Max wing loading 31.64 kg/m² (6.48 lb/sq ft)
Max speed 140 kt (260 km/h)
Stalling speed 33.5 kt (62 km/h)
Min sinking speed at 43 kt (79 km/h) 0.7 m (2.3 ft)/sec
Max rough air speed 86 kt (160 km/h)
Best glide ratio at 51 kt (95 km/h) 34

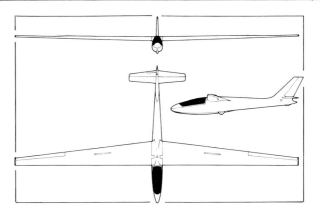

Poland / **SZD-30 Pirat C**

The single-seat Pirat was designed by Jerzy Smielkiewicz as a multi-purpose sailplane capable of fulfilling the needs of every area from training to competition flying and is cleared for cloud flying and basic aerobatics. The prototype flew for the first time on 19 May 1966 and production started in 1967; 1,210 had been completed by the end of 1977.

The high-set wing is in three parts: a plywood-covered multi-spar centre section, and tapered outer panels of single-spar torsion box construction. The ailerons are mass-balanced and double-plate airbrakes are situated on the centre section and operate on both upper and lower surfaces. The fuselage consists of a plywood monocoque structure with a glassfibre nose section and cockpit floor. The cockpit is covered by a sideways hinged blown canopy and incorporates adjustable back rest and rudder pedals. Landing gear consists of a front skid with shock absorber and a non-retractable monowheel. The T-tail is all-wood and includes a tab on the trailing edge of the elevator.

The Pirat C, which first flew in January 1978, features a more roomy cockpit with a larger canopy. The landing wheel has been moved forward and the nose skid removed.

Data   Pirat C
Manufacturer   SZD
First flight   January 1978
Wing span   15.0 m (49 ft 2½ in)
Length   6.92 m (22 ft 8 in)
Height   0.96 m (3 ft 1¾ in)
Wing area   13.8 m² (148.6 sq ft)
Wing section   Wortmann FX-61-168/60-1261
Aspect ratio   16.3
Empty weight   255 kg (562 lb)
Max weight   370 kg (816 lb)
Water ballast   None
Max wing loading   26.8 kg/m² (5.49 lb/sq ft)
Max speed   135 kt (250 km/h)
Stalling speed   32.5 kt (60 km/h)
Min sinking speed at 40 kt (74 km/h)   0.7 m (2.3 ft)/sec
Max rough air speed   77 kt (145 km/h)
Best glide ratio at 45 kt (84 km/h)   34

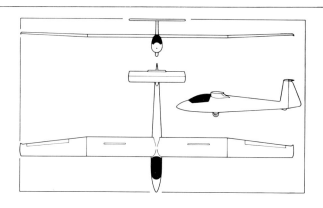

SZD-36A **Cobra 15** / Poland

The SZD-36 Cobra 15 is a single-seat Standard Class high-performance sailplane designed by Dipl. Ing. Wladislaw Okarmus. Design was started in October 1968 and the prototype Cobra 15 flew for the first time on 30 December 1969. In the 1970 World Championships at Marfa, Texas, Polish pilots Wroblewski and Kepka won second and third places in the Standard Class in Cobra 15s, and a Cobra 17 was placed fifth in the Open Class.
The cantilever shoulder-set wings are of single-spar wooden construction with heavy moulded plywood stressed skin covered with glassfibre. The plain ailerons are of plywood/polystyrene foam sandwich construction and are mass-balanced. SZD type metal/glassfibre airbrakes are fitted above and below each wing surface. The 17 metre Open Class Cobra has provision for water ballast in the wings.
The fuselage is an oval section all-wood semi-monocoque structure, ply covered at the rear and glassfibre covered at the front. The one-piece blown canopy slides forward to open. Landing gear consists of a manually retractable monowheel and a tailskid. The all-moving T-tail has the swept back fin and rudder characteristic of the series and later models of the Foka and is fitted with a spring trimmer and geared tab.

Data Cobra 15
Manufacturer SZD
First flight December 1969
Wing span 15.0 m (49 ft 2½ in)
Length 7.05 m (23 ft 1½ in)
Height 1.59 m (5 ft 2¾ in)
Wing area 11.6 m² (124.9 sq ft)
Wing section Wortmann FX-61-168/60-1261
Aspect ratio 19.4
Empty weight 257 kg (567 lb)
Max weight 385 kg (849 lb)
Water ballast None
Max wing loading 33.2 kg/m² (6.8 lb/sq ft)
Max speed 135 kt (250 km/h)
Stalling speed 36 kt (67 km/h)
Min sinking speed at 39.5 kt (73 km/h) 0.6 m (1.97 ft)/sec
Max rough air speed 91.5 kt (170 km/h)
Best glide ratio at 51.5 kt (96 km/h) 38

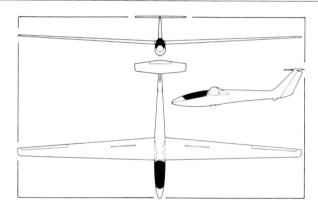

Poland / **SZD-40X Halny**

First flown on 23 December 1972 by Dipl. Ing. Z. Bylock of the Experimental Institute at Bielskobiala, the two-seat high-performance SZD-40X Halny was designed by W. Okarmus and built as a research sailplane to establish the efficiency of a new wing section. This is a 20-metre adaptation of the Zefir 4 wing, which gave excellent performance at high speeds but was less efficient when thermalling in weak lift.

The cantilever shoulder-set wing is a sparless glassfibre/wood box structure with a 4° forward sweep at quarter chord and fittings of stainless steel. It features hingeless flaps and slotless ailerons operated by pushrods.

SZD-type double-plate metal airbrakes, positioned at 60% chord, operate both above and below each wing surface. The fuselage has an all-plastic monocoque front portion, steel tube frame centre portion and metal tube monocoque rear portion. The two tandem seats are covered by a one-piece canopy; the controls and instrument panel are fitted to the rear cockpit only. The T-tail is glassfibre and features spring trimming. The landing gear comprises a retractable monowheel with shoe brake and a fixed tail wheel.

Data Halny
Manufacturer SZD
First flight December 1972
Wing span 20.0 m (65 ft 7½ in)
Length 8.75 m (28 ft 8½ in)
Height 1.8 m (5 ft 11 in)
Wing area 16.11 m² (173.4 sq ft)
Wing section NN-11M
Aspect ratio 24.66
Empty weight 410 kg (904 lb)
Max weight 596 kg (1,314 lb)
Water ballast None
Max wing loading 36.9 kg/m² (7.55 lb/sq ft)
Max speed 130 kt (240 km/h)
Stalling speed 35 kt (65 km/h)
Min sinking speed at 40.5 kt (75 km/h) 0.55 m (1.8 ft)/sec
Best glide ratio at 54 kt (100 km/h) 43

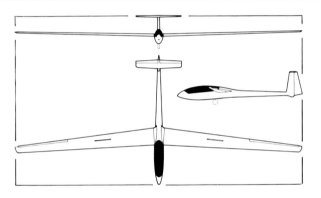

SZD-48 Standard Jantar 2 / Poland

Designed by Adam Kurbiel, the Jantar series was the first Polish excursion into all-glassfibre sailplanes. The SZD-38 Jantar made its first public appearance at the 1972 World Championships at Vrsac, where it gained second place and won the OSTIV cup for the best 19-metre design. In 1973 it broke seven Polish national records. Originally there were two versions of the Jantar: the SZD-38A Open Class Jantar and the SZD-41 Jantar Standard. These have been superseded by the SZD-42 and SZD-48 respectively. The cantilever shoulder-set wings comprise a single-spar ribless structure with a foam-filled glassfibre/epoxy resin sandwich skin. The wings are flapless and DFS-type glassfibre

airbrakes are fitted above and below each wing. There is provision for 150 kg (330 lb) of water ballast in the leading edges. The fuselage consists of an all-glassfibre/epoxy resin shell structure; the centre portion has a steel tube frame coupling together the wings, fuselage and landing gear. The pilot sits in a semi-reclining seat under a two-piece canopy, of which the front section is fixed and the rear section is hinged aft. Landing gear consists of a manually-retractable monowheel with disc brake and a fixed tailwheel.

Data Jantar Standard 2
Manufacturer SZD
First flight December 1977
Wing span 15.0 m (49 ft 2½ in)
Length 6.71 m (22 ft 8½ in)
Wing area 10.66 m² (114.8 sq ft)
Wing section NN-8
Aspect ratio 21.1
Empty weight 247 kg (545 lb)
Max weight 520 kg (1,146 lb)
Water ballast 150 kg (330 lb)
Max wing loading 41.27 kg/m² (8.45 lb/sq ft)
Max speed 167 kt (310 km/h)
Stalling speed 39 kt (72 km/h)
Min sinking speed at 39.4 kt (73 km/h) 0.65 m (2.0 ft)/sec
Max rough air speed 86.5 kt (160 km/h)
Best glide ratio at 70 kt (130 km/h) 40

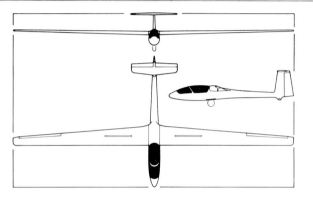

Poland / **SZD-42 Jantar 2B**

This high-performance single-seat Open Class sailplane was developed by Dipl. Ing. Kurbiel from the SZD-38A Jantar 1. It flew for the first time on 2 February 1976. The first two examples were flown by the Polish team in the 1976 World Championships, where they gained second and third places in the Open Class.

The Jantar 2 is of all-glassfibre construction with wings of 20.5 m (67 ft 3 in) span built in four sections for ease of rigging and trailing. The single-spar wings are of ribless construction with foam filled glassfibre/epoxy resin sandwich skin incorporating multi-hinged ailerons and hingeless trailing-edge flaps hung from the upper surfaces.

DFS-type metal airbrakes operate on both upper and lower wing surfaces.

The fuselage is an all-glassfibre/epoxy resin shell structure, the centre portion of which has a steel tube frame which couples the wings, fuselage and landing gear.

The most notable difference between the Jantar 2 and other models in the Jantar series lies in the tail unit, which has been changed from the T-tail arrangement to a conventional configuration comprising stabiliser and elevator. Accommodation is the same as that for the Jantar Standard.

Data Jantar 2B
Manufacturer SZD
First flight February 1976
Wing span 20.15 m (66 ft 1¼ in)
Length 7.11 m (23 ft 4 in)
Height 1.56 m (5 ft 1½ in)
Wing area 14.25 m² (153.4 sq ft)
Wing section Wortmann FX-67-K-170/150
Aspect ratio 29.2
Empty weight 355 kg (783 lb)
Max weight 645 kg (1,422 lb)
Water ballast 170 kg (375 lb)
Max wing loading 45.3 kg/m² (9.28 lb/sq ft)
Max speed 151 kt (280 km/h)
Stalling speed 35 kt (65 km/h)
Min sinking speed at 40.5 kt (75 km/h) 0.45 m (1.48 ft)/sec
Max rough air speed 108 kt (200 km/h)
Best glide ratio at 57 kt (105 km/h) 48

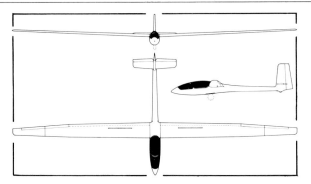

SZD-45A Ogar / Poland

The SZD-45A Ogar (Greyhound) is a two-seat motor glider for ab initio and advanced training and cross-country flying. Designed by Dipl. Ing. Tadeusz Labuc the Ogar made its first flight on 29 May 1973.

Of unusual appearance this sailplane has a fuselage of the pod and boom type. The main nacelle structure comprises a glassfibre/epoxy resin shell on two strong wooden frames which carry the wings, engine mounting, fuel tank and the tubular duralumin boom which supports the cantilever T-tail. The wing is a single-spar wooden structure with a moulded plywood stressed skin covered with glassfibre. The slotless ailerons are of glassfibre sandwich construction and are controlled by pushrods. Airbrakes are fitted above and below each wing. Landing gear consists of a semi-retractable monowheel with shock absorber and disc brake and fully castoring tailwheel.

The two seats are arranged side-by-side beneath a two-piece upward-hinged canopy. Dual controls are fitted as standard. The power plant is a 50.7 kW (68 hp) Limbach SL 1700 EC four-cylinder engine, mounted behind the cabin, driving a two-blade Hoffmann pusher propeller.

Data Ogar
Manufacturer SZD
First flight May 1973
Wing span 17.53 m (57 ft 6¼ in)
Length 7.95 m (26 ft 1 in)
Height 1.72 m (5 ft 7¾ in)
Wing area 19.1 m² (205.6 sq ft)
Wing section Wortmann FX-61-168/1261
Aspect ratio 16.2
Empty weight 470 kg (1,036 lb)
Max weight 700 kg (1,543 lb)
Water ballast None
Max wing loading 36.6 kg/m² (7.49 lb/sq ft)
Max level speed at S/L 97 kt (180 km/h)
Stalling speed 37 kt (68 km/h)
Min sinking speed at 39 kt (72 km/h) 0.96 m (3.15 ft)/sec
Best glide ratio at 54 kt (100 km/h) 27.5
Power plant Limbach SL 1700 EC, 50.7 kW (68 hp)

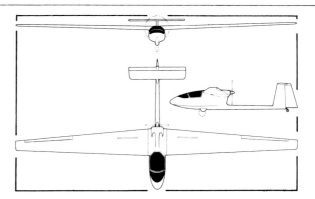

T-O run 200 m (656 ft)
Max rate of climb at S/L 168 m (551 ft)/min
Range 550 km (296 nm)

Poland / **SZD-50 Puchacz 2**

Using experience gained in the design of the SZD-50 Dromader 1, which flew in 1976, Dipl.Ing. Adam Meus has developed the Puchacz as a successor to the well known Bocian. The Puchacz 2 is a two-seat high-performance training sailplane designed to provide easy pilot conversion to modern sailplanes.

The Puchacz is of conventional glassfibre construction, with wings and landing gear fitting into a central wooden frame. The mid-set, forward-swept wings incorporate airbrakes on their top and bottom surfaces. The conventional tail unit has a hinged elevator and fabric-covered rudder. Two towing hooks are provided, one in the nose for aerotowing and the other at the centre of gravity for winch launching. The roomy cockpit incorporates two seats in tandem beneath a one-piece, side-hinged canopy. Dual controls and front-seat instrumentation are fitted; the instruments are easily visible from the rear seat, which can be moved fore and aft. The rudder pedals are adjustable in flight. The landing gear consists of a non-retractable mainwheel situated behind the centre of gravity and fitted with a shock-absorber and disc brake, and a small fixed nosewheel. The tail skid can be replaced by a tailwheel.

Data Puchacz 2
Manufacturer SZD
First flight December 1977
Wing span 16.67 m (54 ft 8 in)
Length 8.38 m (29 ft 10 in)
Height 1.92 m (6 ft 10½ in)
Wing area 18.16 m² ((195.5 sq ft)
Wing section Wortmann
Aspect ratio 15.3
Empty weight 331 kg (730 lb)
Max weight 550 kg (1,216 lb)
Water ballast None
Max wing loading 30.3 kg/m² (6.2 lb/sq ft)
Max speed 119 kt (220 km/h)
Stalling speed 60 kt (110 km/h)
Min sinking speed at 40 kt (75 km/h) 0.7 m (2.3 ft)/sec
Max rough air speed 81 kt (150 km/h)
Best glide ratio at 52 kt (96 km/h) 30

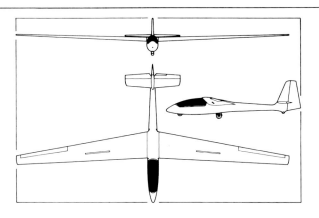

ICA-Brasov IS-28B2 / Romania

The IS-28B2 is an improved version of the 15-metre IS-28, the two-seat high-performance sailplane designed by Dipl. Ing. Iosif Silimon and his team, from which it differs primarily in having 17-metre span all-metal wings, a longer and more slender fuselage and reduced wing and tailplane dihedral. The original IS-28, which first flew in August 1970, had a glide ratio of 25 and minimum sink speed of 0.85 m/sec (2.79 ft/sec).

The current production B2 version is of all-metal construction. The mid-set wings are attached to the fuselage by two adjustable tapered bolts at the leading edge and two fixed tapered bolts at the trailing edge. Schempp-Hirth metal airbrakes are mounted above and below each wing surface. The ailerons and camber-changing flaps, which operate between +15° and −11°, are fabric covered except for the leading edges. The fuselage is an all-metal semi-monocoque structure of oval cross section. Seating for two persons is arranged in tandem under a one-piece Plexiglas canopy which hinges sideways.

The folding cantilever T-tail is similar to that of the IS-28 but with single-spar fin. Landing gear consists of a semi-retractable monowheel with shock absorber and disc brake, and a sprung tailskid.

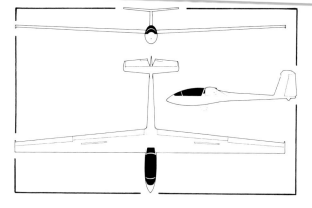

Data   IS-28B2
Manufacturer   ICA-Brasov
First flight   April 1973
Wing span   17.0 m (55 ft 9¼ in)
Length   8.17 m (26 ft 9½ in)
Height   1.8 m (5 ft 10¾ in)
Wing area   18.24 m² (196.4 sq ft)
Wing section   Wortmann FX-61-163/60-126
Aspect ratio   15.8
Empty weight   330 kg (728 lb)
Max weight   590 kg (1,301 lb)
Water ballast   None
Max wing loading   32.34 kg/m² (6.62 lb/sq ft)
Max speed   144 kt (266 km/h)
Stalling speed (two-seat)   39 kt (72 km/h)
Min sinking speed at 39 kt (72 km/h)   0.69 m (2.26 ft)/sec
Max rough air speed   89 kt (136 km/h)
Best glide ratio at 54 kt (100 km/h)   34

Romania / **ICA-Brasov IS-28M2**

Designed to Romanian civil airworthiness regulations and complying with OSTIV requirements, the IS-28M2 is of interest both to the gliding and the power flying fraternities. An all-metal motor glider with T-tail, the prototype flew for the first time on 26 June 1976 and made its international public debut at the Farnborough International air show in September.

The cantilever low-set wings are of mainly metal construction and are swept forward 2° 30′ at quarter chord. The flaps can be set to a negative position to aid high-speed flying between thermals; all-metal Hütter airbrakes are fitted to the upper wing surfaces. The fuselage is a conventional structure built in three parts: an oval front section built up on two longerons and cross frames; an aluminium alloy monocoque centre portion; and a rear portion of aluminium alloy frames and skin. The broad cockpit contains side-by-side seating and dual controls, including two throttles and two airbrake levers.

The landing gear consists of a semi-retractable two-wheel main gear, mounted at the inboard ends of the wings and integral with the fuselage, and incorporating shock absorption and brakes, and a steerable tailwheel. The power plant is a Limbach SL 1700 E1 driving a Hoffman two-blade variable-pitch fully feathering propeller.

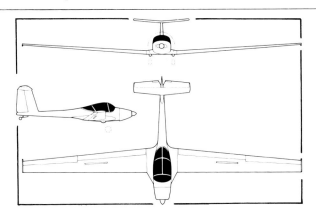

Data IS-28M2
Manufacturer ICA-Brasov
First flight June 1976
Wing span 17.0 m (55 ft 9¼ in)
Length 7.5 m (24 ft 7¼ in)
Height 2.15 m (7 ft 0¾ ft)
Wing area 18.24 m² (196.4 sq ft)
Wing section Wortmann FX-61-163/60-126
Aspect ratio 15.8
Empty weight 530 kg (1,168 lb)
Max weight 745 kg (1,642 lb)
Water ballast None
Max wing loading 40.84 kg/m² (8.36 lb/sq ft)
Max level speed 108 kt (200 km/h)
Stalling speed 35 kt (65 km/h)
Min sinking speed at 43 kt (80 km/h) 0.87 m (2.85 ft)/sec
Best glide ratio at 54 kt (100 km/h) 29
Power plant Limbach SL 1700 EI, 50.7 kW (68 hp)
T-O run 160 m (525 ft)
Max rate of climb at S/L 186 m (610 ft)/min
Range 450 km (243 nm)

ICA-Brasov IS-29 / Romania

The IS-29, designed under the leadership of Dip. Ing. Iosif Silimon, can be adapted to suit a variety of requirements or weather conditions. All versions have an identical fuselage and tail unit and a choice of wings is available.

The IS-29B Standard Class version has all-wood wings of 15 metre (49 ft 2½ in) span and was first flown in April 1970. The IS-29D Standard Class sailplane has all-metal wings and was first flown in November 1970. The current production model is the IS-29D2 which features an improved cockpit and controls, Hütter airbrakes, separate tailplane and elevator and improved rigging system. The IS-29D4, introduced in 1977, has provision for water ballast but no airbrakes.

The IS-29E is a high-performance Open Class version with wings of increased span which feature flaps and Schempp-Hirth airbrakes and integral water ballast tanks. Current production model is the IS-29E3 with 20 m (65 ft 7½ in) span wings; a 19 m (62 ft 4 in) span version, the IS-29E2, was under development in 1977. The IS-29G Club version, with all-metal wings of 16.5 m (54 ft 1½ in) span, first flew in 1972.

All versions feature all-metal construction, except where previously mentioned, cantilever T-tail, retractable landing gear and single adjustable seat under a two-piece canopy.

Data IS-29D2
Manufacturer ICA-Brasov
First flight November 1970
Wing span 15.0 m (49 ft 2½ in)
Length 7.38 m (24 ft 2½ in)
Height 1.68 m (5 ft 6¼ in)
Wing area 10.4 m² (112 sq ft)
Wing section Wortmann FX-61-165/124
Aspect ratio 21.5
Empty weight 235 kg (518 lb)
Max weight 360 kg (794 lb)
Water ballast None
Max wing loading 34.62 kg/m² (7.09 lb/sq ft)
Max speed 135 kt (250 km/h)
Stalling speed 36.5 kt (67 km/h)
Min sinking speed at 43 kt (80 km/h) 0.43 m (1.41 ft)/sec
Best glide ratio at 50 kt (93 km/h) 38

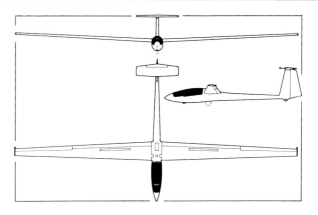

Romania / **ICA-Brasov IS-32**

First shown publicly at the 1977 Paris Air Show, the IS-28 tandem two-seat Open Class sailplane is developed from the IS-28B2 and flew for the first time in June 1977.

The IS-32 uses the fuselage of the IS-28B but an entirely new wing of 20 m (65 ft 7½ in) span has been developed and the tail unit has been redesigned. The interconnected flaps and ailerons, which are now being referred to as 'flaperons', work in conjunction with and improve the action of the ailerons in negative position for high-speed cruising, and in positive position for thermalling, but disconnect for landing. The wings are also fitted with large Schempp-Hirth airbrakes and water ballast tanks.

Although the fuselage is similar to that of the 28B, a new undercarriage has been fitted which includes a fully-retractable main wheel. The T-tail has been redesigned with a one-piece tailplane using a new thinner aerofoil section and is set at 0° incidence.

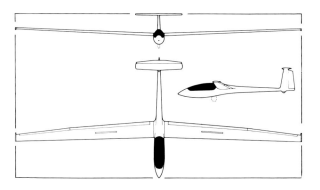

Data IS-32
Manufacturer ICA-Brasov
First flight June 1977
Wing span 20.0 m (65 ft 7½ in)
Length 8.36 m (27 ft 5¼ in)
Wing area 14.68 m² (158 sq ft)
Aspect ratio 27.24
Empty weight 350 kg (772 lb)
Max weight 590 lb (1,301 lb)
Water ballast None
Max wing loading 40.6 kg/m² (8.31 lb/sq ft)
Max speed 125 kt (232 km/h)
Stalling speed 40 kt (74 km/h)
Min sinking speed at 46 kt (85 km/h) 0.53 m (1.74 ft)/sec
Best glide ratio at 53 kt (98 km/h) 46

Beatty-Johl BJ-3 / South Africa

The BJ- series of sailplanes are unusual in that they are designed for a particular climate. From experience gained with the successful BJ-2 Mr P. J. Beatty of Johannesburg built the BJ-3, designed by Mr W. A. T. Johl especially to take advantage of the strong South African thermals. First flight was in 1965 and on 28 December 1967 the BJ-3 set up an international speed record over a 500 km triangular course of 135.32 km/hr (73.01 kt).

Construction is almost entirely of metal, only the forward part of the fuselage being glassfibre. The wings are of dural secured with round-headed rivets to a wide spar; this structure is then covered with polystyrene foam and glassfibre applied to the upper surface to achieve a smooth finish. Like the BJ-2 this aircraft uses Fowler flaps which, when extended, increase the wing area by 30% and can be lowered to a maximum of 30°. Four sets of DFS-type double airbrakes are fitted. The retractable landing wheel with brake is situated behind the centre of gravity.

The BJ-3A was developed from the BJ-3 in 1968, followed by the BJ-4, which features a new fuselage and tail unit and uses the existing BJ-3 wings. The original T-tail was replaced by a tall perpendicular fin with an all-flying tailplane located on the fuselage behind the rudder. Two BJ-4s were built for the 1970 World Championships.

Data BJ-3
Manufacturer Beatty-Johl
First flight 1965
Wing span 16.15 m (52 ft 11¾ in)
Length 7.5 m (24 ft 7¼ in)
Wing area 12.3 m² (132.4 sq ft)
Wing section NACA 66₁212/0009-64A-0.8
Aspect ratio 20.0
Max weight 522 kg (1,151 lb)
Water ballast None
Max wing loading 42.44 kg/m² (8.69 lb/sq ft)
Max speed 154 kt (285 km/h)
Stalling speed 28.5 kt (53 km/h)
Min sinking speed at 40 kt (74 km/h) 0.67 m (2.2 ft)/sec
Max rough air speed 120 kt (222 km/h)
Best glide ratio at 70 kt (130 km/h) 40

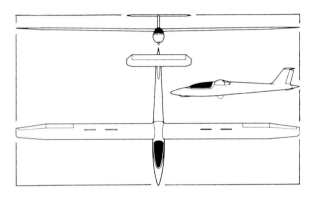

Switzerland / **FFA Diamant**

The Diamant is, as is expected from the Swiss, a beautiful piece of precision engineering. It is a true all-glassfibre sailplane in that every part is made of that material (while most 'glassfibre' sailplanes use plywood and balsa in their construction). Only the flying control system and fittings are of other materials.

The fuselage and tail unit were developed at the Swiss Federal Institute of Technology in Zürich under the direction of Professor Rauscher. A prototype fuselage was built in 1962 and flew with Ka 6CR wings, receiving the designation Ka-Bi-Vo.

FFA gradually took over development and manufacture of the Diamant, starting with the HBV-Diamant 15, which used H301 Libelle wings and which first flew on 5 September 1964. Thirteen of this type were built. The Diamant 16.5 is generally similar to the HBV-Diamant 15 but has wings of increased span, designed and built by FFA. A total of 41 had been built when production ended. The Diamant 18 is generally similar to the 16.5 but has wings of 18 m (59 ft 0½ in). Accommodation is in a semi-reclining position beneath a forward-sliding canopy. Early models featured a side stick, mounted on the right hand side, but this was moved to the more conventional central position on later models.

Data Diamant 18
Manufacturer Flug und Fahrzeugwerke
First flight February 1968
Wing span 18.0 m (59 ft 0½ in)
Height 1.35 m (4 ft 5 in)
Length 7.72 m (25 ft 4 in)
Wing area 14.28 m² (154 sq ft)
Wing section Wortmann FX-62-Z-153 mod.
Aspect ratio 22.7
Empty weight 280 kg (617 lb)
Max weight 440 kg (970 lb)
Water ballast None
Max wing loading 30.8 kg/m² (6.31 lb/sq ft)
Max speed 129 kt (240 km/h)
Stalling speed 32.5 kt (60 km/h)
Min sinking speed at 39 kt (72 km/h) 0.52 m (1.71 ft)/sec
Max rough air speed 108 kt (200 km/h)
Best glide ratio at 54 kt (100 km/h) 45

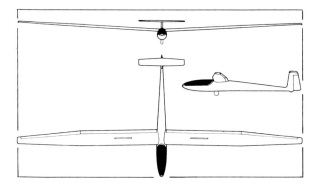

Hegetschweiler Moswey 3 / Switzerland

Designed by Georg Müller, the Moswey series of sailplanes was one of the most significant to emerge from Switzerland during the 25 years following 1930. The Moswey 1, a strutted high-wing training glider of 13.25 m (43 ft 6 in) span, was followed in 1935 by the Moswey 2, with its cantilever, mid-set gull wings of 13.8 m (45 ft 3 in) span. Two years later this sailplane took part in the first International Championships in Germany. The Moswey 2A is a version in which the wing span was increased to 15.5 m (49 ft 10 in). Introduced in 1943, the Moswey 3 met the demand for a small aerobatic sailplane. Like the 2A, the Moswey 3 is made of traditional plywood and fabric, though the wing span is reduced to 14.0 m (45 ft 11 in). In 1948 the Moswey 3 came third in the World Championships and in the same year, flown by Siegbert Maurer, made the first south-north crossing of the Alps. After the war the Moswey 3 held almost all the Swiss national records and set the first world record for the 100 km triangle. Fourteen 3s were built before the type was superseded by the Moswey 4 in 1950.

The Moswey 4, though similar in construction, features a more roomy cockpit, a wing span of 14.4 m (47 ft 3 in) and an unusually large Plexiglas canopy giving excellent visibility.

Data Moswey 3
Manufacturer Hegetschweiler
First flight October 1943
Wing span 14.0 m (45 ft 11 in)
Length 6.0 m (19 ft 8 in)
Height 1.4 m (4 ft 7 in)
Wing area 13.1 m² (141 sq ft)
Wing section Göttingen 535
Aspect ratio 15.0
Empty weight 160 kg (353 lb)
Max weight 250 kg (551 lb)
Water ballast None
Max wing loading 19.1 kg/m² (3.9 lb/sq ft)
Max speed 113 kt (210 km/h)
Stalling speed 27 kt (50 km/h)
Min sinking speed at 32 kt (60 km/h) 0.65 m (2.1 ft)/sec
Max rough air speed 67 kt (125 km/h)
Best glide ratio at 38 kt (70 km/h) 27.5

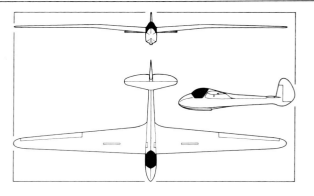

Switzerland / **Neukom AN-66C Super-Elfe**

This excursion into the field of variable-geometry wing design was Albert Neukom's answer to a request to build the best sailplane in the world. He designed and built it entirely on his own, incorporating some quite innovative technical details, the most striking of which was the chain-operated variable wing flaps, operated by a crank in the cockpit. The 23 m (75 ft 5½ in) three-piece wings are constructed of riveted light alloy double T-spars with vacuum pressed plywood sandwich outer skins. The centre section is 6.5 m (21 ft 4 in) in length, the two outer panels each 8.25 m (27 ft 0¾ in) in length. Neukom's specially designed combination of flaps can increase the wing area by 20% when fully extended, at the same time changing the profile so that when either fully extended or fully retracted (the only two possible positions) a continuous Eppler profile is achieved. Water ballast is carried in the wing centre section.

The fuselage, like that of the earlier AN-66B, has a front section of glassfibre and a rear section of plywood and balsa sandwich. The V-tail of earlier aircraft in the series has given way on the AN-66C to a conventional tail unit with hinged elevator.

In 1974 a second machine was produced with a four-piece wing of 21 m (68 ft 11 in) span, designated AN-66D.

Data   AN-66C
Manufacturer   Neukom
First flight   September 1973
Wing span   23.0 m (75 ft 5½ in)
Length   8.1 m (26 ft 6¾ in)
Height   1.85 m (6 ft 0¾ in)
Wing area   16.0 m² (172.0 sq ft)
Wing section   Eppler 562/569
Aspect ratio   33.0
Empty weight   420 kg (926 lb)
Max weight   650 kg (1,433 lb)
Water ballast   60 kg (132 lb)
Max wing loading   33.1 kg/m² (6.8 lb/sq ft)
Max speed   146 kt (270 km/h)
Stalling speed   32.5 kt (60 km/h)
Min sinking speed at 40.5 kt (75 km/h)   0.5 m (1.64 ft)/sec
Best glide ratio at 48.5 kt (90 km/h)   48

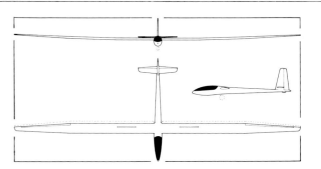

Neukom Standard Elfe S-3 / Switzerland

Shortly after the Second World War Albert Neukom brought out a diminutive sailplane aptly named the Elfe 1. It had a wing span of only 9 m (29 ft 6¼ in) and an empty weight of 43 kg (95 lb). The span was later increased to 11 m (36 ft 1 in). During 1946–47 Dr W. Pfenninger designed the Elfe 2 with camber-changing flaps and a span of 15.4 m (50 ft 6¼ in); sink rate was 0.5 m (1.64 ft)/sec and best glide ratio was 37. The Elfe PM3 of 1951, with 16 m (52 ft 6 in) span wings, was disappointingly heavy and was succeeded by the laminar-winged Elfe M.

The S-1 prototype of the Standard Elfe first flew on 1 May 1964 and featured a V-tail. The Standard Elfe 2 had a conventional tail unit, with the tailplane at the base of the fin. The production-type S-3, first flown in May 1966, has the tailplane mounted part-way up the fin.

The wing, which is built in three parts, is of balsa-plywood sandwich construction and is fitted with trailing edge airbrakes. The fuselage and tail are of glassfibre and plywood sandwich construction. The landing gear comprises a rubber-sprung retractable monowheel with brake.

Flown by Markus Ritzi, a Standard Elfe gained second place in the 1965 World Championships. In the Standard Class competition at the 1968 World Championships, an Elfe S-3 flown by Andrew Smith of the USA was placed first.

Data Standard Elfe S-3
Manufacturer Neukom
First flight May 1966
Wing span 15.0 m (49 ft 2½ in)
Length 7.30 m (23 ft 11½ in)
Height 1.50 m (4 ft 11 in)
Wing area 11.9 m² (128.1 sq ft)
Wing section Wortmann FX Series
Aspect ratio 19.0
Empty weight 208 kg (459 lb)
Max weight 320 kg (705 lb)
Water ballast None
Max wing loading 26.89 kg/m² (5.5 lb/sq ft)
Max speed 129.5 kt (240 km/h)
Stalling speed 30 kt (55 km/h)
Min sinking speed at 40 kt (74 km/h) 0.64 m (2.1 ft)/sec
Max rough air speed 108 kt (200 km/h)
Best glide ratio at 51 kt (95 km/h) 37.5

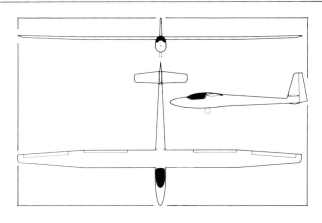

The S-4A Elfe 15 is a developed version of the Standard Class S-3, from which it differs principally by having a new two-piece strengthened wing fitted with Schempp-Hirth airbrakes, and a more roomy all-plastic forward fuselage of improved aerodynamic shape. The prototype flew for the first time in 1970.

The Elfe 17 is a 17 metre Open Class version of the S-4A, employing the same fuselage, but having a two-piece wing of increased span. A maximum of 60 kg (132 lb) of water ballast can be carried in the wing leading edge.

The wings of both versions have an aluminium alloy main spar surrounded by a plywood and foam sandwich. The fuselage and tail unit are of glassfibre and plywood/foam sandwich construction. The landing gear consists of a rubber-sprung retractable monowheel with brake.

Both sailplanes are available as either finished aircraft, assembled but unpainted and unfinished, or as a kit of parts.

Data Elfe 17
Manufacturer Neukom
First flight 1970
Wing span 17.0 m (55 ft 9¼ in)
Length 7.1 m (23 ft 3½ in)
Height 1.50 m (4 ft 11 in)
Wing area 13.2 m² (142.1 sq ft)
Wing section Wortmann FX-61-163/60-126
Aspect ratio 21.8
Empty weight 255 kg (562 lb)
Max weight 380 kg (838 lb)
Water ballast 60 kg (132 lb)
Max wing loading 28.8 kg/m² (5.9 lb/sq ft)
Max speed 113 kt (210 km/h)
Stalling speed 35 kt (65 km/h)
Min sinking speed at 40.5 kt (75 km/h) 0.56 m (1.84 ft)/sec
Max rough air speed 113 kt (210 km/h)
Best glide ratio at 48.5 kt (90 km/h) 39

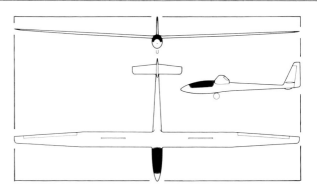

Pilatus B4-PC11 / Switzerland

The Pilatus B4 is a popular all-metal single-seat Standard Class sailplane. It is suitable both for pilots who have just soloed because of its simple handling characteristics and for the more experienced who appreciate its good performance. The prototype, the B-4 was designed by Ingo Herbot as a private venture and first flew in 1966. Pilatus took over and developed this design and the first flight of the B4-PC11 was made in 1972.

The cantilever shoulder wings are in two parts and are built up on a light alloy U-shaped main spar to which the large skin panels are attached by a single row of countersunk rivets. The fuselage is a semi-monocoque structure of light alloy with flush riveting. The roomy cockpit contains a single semi-reclining seat and is covered by a one-piece canopy. The landing gear consists of a non-retractable main wheel (optionally retractable) and fixed tail wheel in tandem. The main wheel is faired by doors when retracted. The cantilever T-tail is constructed from light alloy with PVC ribs. Elevator trimming is by means of a bias spring.

In 1978 the manufacturing and sales rights for the B-4 were acquired by Nippi of Japan, which builds the NP-100 Albatross.

Data B4-PC11
Manufacturer Pilatus
First flight 1972
Wing span 15.0 m (49 ft 2½ in)
Length 6.57 m (21 ft 6¾ in)
Height 1.57 m (5 ft 1¾ in)
Wing area 14.04 m² (151.1 sq ft)
Wing section NACA 64₃618
Aspect ratio 16.0
Empty weight 230 kg (507 lb)
Max weight 350 kg (772 lb)
Water ballast None
Max wing loading 24.93 kg/m² (5.1 lb/sq ft)
Max speed 129.5 kt (240 km/h)
Stalling speed 33.5 kt (62 km/h)
Min sinking speed at 39 kt (72 km/h) 0.64 m (2.1 ft)/sec
Max rough air speed 129.5 kt (240 km/h)
Best glide ratio at 46 kt (85 km/h) 35

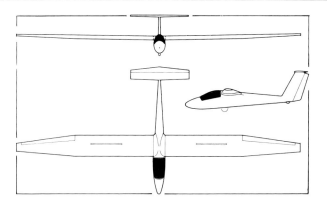

United Kingdom / **EoN Olympia**

The EoN Olympia is an improved version of the German DFS Meise. It was built by Elliotts of Newbury where the late chairman, Mr H.G.C. Buckingham, wishing to use the experience gained during the war when the company manufactured transport gliders and sub-assemblies for many different types of aircraft, entered into co-production with Chiltern Aircraft to build a modernised version of the Meise. Production started at Newbury in 1946 and the prototype first flew in January 1947.

Many of the design features which made the Meise famous for its good flying qualities are retained in the Olympia. Its high-set cantilever wood and fabric wings incorporate D-spars in the leading edge and fabric-covered wooden ailerons. DFS-type airbrakes are fitted. A luggage compartment is built into the fuselage with access on the port side under the wing root. The Olympia 2 has a fixed landing wheel and the Olympia 3 is similar to the Olympia 1 but is fitted with a jettisonable dolly wheel.

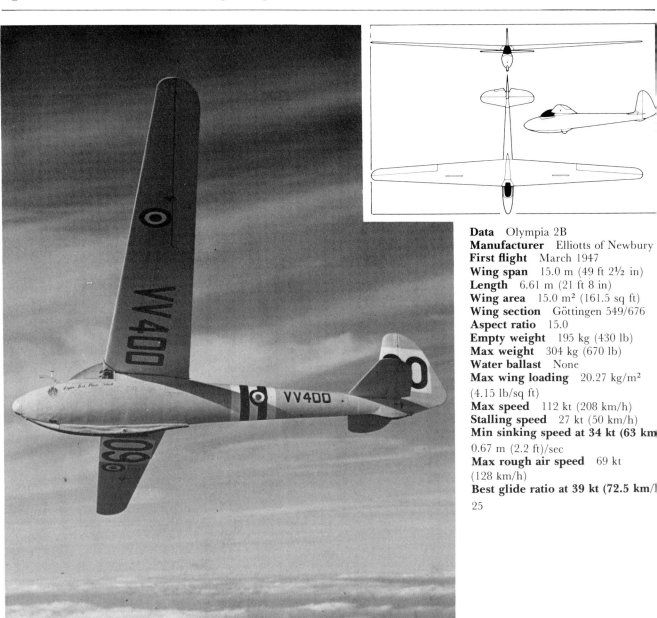

Data   Olympia 2B
Manufacturer   Elliotts of Newbury
First flight   March 1947
Wing span   15.0 m (49 ft 2½ in)
Length   6.61 m (21 ft 8 in)
Wing area   15.0 m² (161.5 sq ft)
Wing section   Göttingen 549/676
Aspect ratio   15.0
Empty weight   195 kg (430 lb)
Max weight   304 kg (670 lb)
Water ballast   None
Max wing loading   20.27 kg/m²
(4.15 lb/sq ft)
Max speed   112 kt (208 km/h)
Stalling speed   27 kt (50 km/h)
Min sinking speed at 34 kt (63 km
0.67 m (2.2 ft)/sec
Max rough air speed   69 kt
(128 km/h)
Best glide ratio at 39 kt (72.5 km/
25

The EoN 463 is a single-seat Standard Class sailplane, developed from the 460, of which only five were built. The wings of the 460 and 463 are of wooden construction with light alloy spars, aerodynamically similar to those of the 419 but reduced in span to 15 m, with the aileron span reduced by 1.5 m at the wingtip. The fabric/stringer top fairing on the 460 fuselage has been replaced with one of glassfibre. The nose section is also of glassfibre construction instead of plywood and a new canopy has been fitted. The fuselage, like that of the 460, is of the fabric-covered Warren girder type. The landing gear consists of a fixed landing wheel but no nose skid. The tailplane is fitted with conventional elevators,

and the whole assembly can be folded up for trailing.

The EoN 463 was first flown in 1963 and proved to be very popular with both clubs and private owners. In 1965 two 465s were built in an attempt to improve the performance in competition flying. Several modifications were incorporated, including a reduced fuselage cross-section area.

Forty-eight 463s were built before Elliots' management, reviewing the company's activities, elected to close the glider section.

Data 463
Manufacturer Elliots of Newbury
First flight April 1963
Wing span 15.0 m (49 ft 2½ in)
Length 6.4 m (21 ft 0 in)
Wing area 12.26 m² (132 sq ft)
Wing section NACA 64³618/421
Aspect ratio 18.0
Empty weight 181 kg (400 lb)
Max weight 286 kg (630 lb)
Water ballast None
Max wing loading 23.33 kg/m² (4.78 lb/sq ft)
Max speed 117.5 kt (218 km/h)
Stalling speed 30 kt (56 km/h)
Min sinking speed at 37 kt (69 km/h) 0.67 m (2.2 ft)/sec
Max rough air speed 74 kt (137 km/h)
Best glide ratio at 42 kt (78 km/h) 32

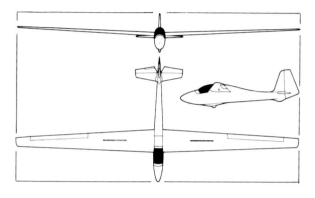

United Kingdom / **Ginn-Lesniak Kestrel**

The tandem two-seat semi-aerobatic Kestrel was designed in 1956 by Mr Lesniak and construction was begun by the designer and Mr Vic Ginn at Dunstable Gliding Club's workshops. The aircraft, however, was abandoned and after a gap of some years was rescued from destruction by Messrs Ron Dodd and Jeff Butt. Mr Dodd, a chartered engineer who had worked at the Royal Aircraft Establishment, Farnborough, recalculated, modified and improved the construction, and with Mr Butt completed the construction, producing a professional-looking two-seat sailplane.

The Kestrel is of conventional wood and fabric construction with metal bonded reinforcement at the wing roots. The two-part wings incorporate large Schempp-Hirth airbrakes and Frise ailerons. The fuselage is all wood with plywood/balsa sandwich reinforcement from the nose cone to just aft of the cockpit. A large skid block protects the nose. A two-piece canopy covers the roomy cockpit, the transparent detachable aft half of which is secured by the fore section, which is a complete Skylark 4 canopy and is hinged sideways. The Kestrel flew for the first time in July 1969 at Enstone.

Data Ginn-Lesniak Kestrel
Manufacturer R. Dodd & J. Butt
First flight July 1969
Wing span 18.0 m (59 ft 0½ in)
Length 7.54 m (24 ft 8¾ in)
Wing area 22.57 m² (243 sq ft)
Wing section Göttingen 549/M12
Aspect ratio 14.3
Empty weight 308 kg (680 lb)
Max weight 499 kg (1,100 lb)
Water ballast None
Max wing loading 22.21 kg/m² (4.55 lb/sq ft)
Max speed 85 kt (158 km/h)
Stalling speed 32.5 kt (60 km/h)
Min sinking speed at 43 kt (80 km/h) 0.67 m (2.2 ft)/sec
Max rough air speed 71.5 kt (133 km/h)
Best glide ratio 28

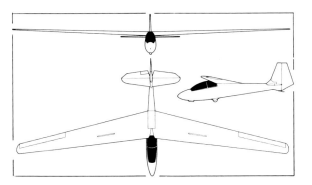

Kenneth Holmes KH-1 / United Kingdom

The KH-1 is a high-performance sailplane of homebuilt construction, and was entirely designed and built by Mr Kenneth Holmes, a meteorologist. Design began in 1968, construction started in the following year and the KH-1 flew for the first time on 24 November 1971.

The cantilever shoulder-set wings are of wood with single aluminium spars joined to plywood webs by epoxy-resin bonding and pop rivets. The closely spaced ribs are covered by a pre-moulded ply/balsa sandwich to 50% chord; aft of this point the covering is 2 mm thick plywood for a further 20% chord and the final 30% is fabric covered. No spoilers are fitted but small-span trailing edge airbrake/flaps are fitted to the inboard section of the wing.

The low profile fuselage is of birch ply covering spruce longerons and plywood frames. The tailplane includes a large fin and rudder of conventional configuration and incorporates an all-moving tailplane with anti-balance tabs controlled by a spring trimmer in the cockpit. The landing gear comprises a retractable monowheel and tail bumper. A tail parachute is fitted for control during approach and for speed limiting purposes.

A second version of the KH-1 has been built by John Halford, named the J.S.H. Scorpion (photo below). It first flew in July 1977.

Data   KH-1
Manufacturer   Kenneth Holmes
First flight   November 1971
Wing span   18.5 m (60 ft 8½ in)
Length   7.24 m (23 ft 9 in)
Height   1.52 m (5 ft 0 in)
Wing area   11.15 m² (120 sq ft)
Wing section   Wortmann FX-61-184/60-126
Aspect ratio   31.0
Empty weight   222 kg (490 lb)
Max weight   322 kg (710 lb)
Water ballast   None
Max wing loading   28.9 kg/m² (5.92 lb/sq ft)
Max speed   84.5 kt (157 km/h)
Stalling speed   36 kt (67 km/h)
Max rough air speed   75 kt (139 km/h)
Best glide ratio at 48 kt (89 km/h)   37

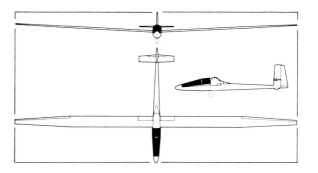

United Kingdom / **Manuel Hawk**

Mr W.L. Manuel, previously noted for a number of sailplane designs which culminated in the Willow Wren of 1932, designed and built the Hawk glider as a project during his retirement. It was built at Fairoaks airfield in Surrey during 1968-1970 and was first flown at the College of Aeronautics at Cranfield on 25 November 1972. After some modifications, including increased rudder area, removal of the airbrakes from the lower wing surfaces and an alteration to the aileron controls, the aircraft is again flying.

The Hawk is a single-seat sailplane designed for soaring in weak thermal conditions. The conventional three-piece wing consists of a spruce spar with plywood leading edge torsion box and fabric covering aft of the main spar. The fuselage is a conventional semi-monocoque structure of plywood-covered spruce. The unusual canopy is in three pieces: the front and rear sections are fixed transparent one-piece single curves; the middle section, which is hinged, is a framed double curve. The aircraft is beautifully finished with a high polish on the natural wood and clear dope on the fabric.

Data Hawk
Manufacturer W.L Manuel
First flight November 1972
Wing span 12.8 m (42 ft 0 in)
Length 6.25 m (20 ft 6 in)
Wing area 13.84 m² (149 sq ft)
Wing section Wortmann FX-61-184/210
Aspect ratio 11.88
Empty weight 184 kg (406 lb)
Max weight 290 kg (639 lb)
Water ballast None
Max wing loading 20.95 kg/m² (4.29 lb/sq ft)
Max speed 78.5 kt (146 km/h)
Stalling speed 31 kt (57.5 km/h)
Min sinking speed at 33 kt (61 km/h) 0.77 m (2.53 ft)/sec
Max rough air speed 64 kt (118.5 km/h)
Best glide ratio at 36 kt (66.5 km/h) 25

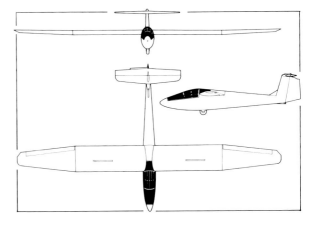

Manuel Condor / United Kingdom

Mr W.L. Manuel, designer of the Willow Wren and more recently the Hawk, disturbed by the loss of lives in hang gliders, has in the Condor provided the answer to those desiring to fly but who have not the financial means to invest in highly priced gliders or the necessary skills to build a modern complex design.

The Condor looks unconventional with its metal tube fuselage and steel control cables, but it provides comfortable side-by-side seating arrangement, open to the elements. It is designed especially for hill soaring and has already made several long flights. The tail unit is a large structure of fabric-covered ribs and a tailplane with wide-chord elevators. Aluminium tubes connect the tail unit to the cockpit section, which is shaped like a boat. The high-set wings are connected to a keel under the cockpit by V-shaped struts on each side. The landing gear consists of a bow-shaped ash skid, using rubber rollers as shock absorbers.

The designer does not provide a figure for minimum sink because, in his own words: 'It is designed to go up, and only sometimes will concede to gravity for landing.'

Data Condor
Manufacturer Manuel, Inwood & Inwood
First flight August 1976
Wing span 15.3 m (50 ft 2½ in)
Length 6.4 m (21 ft 0 in)
Wing area 23.23 m² (250 sq ft)
Wing section Göttingen 462
Aspect ratio 10.0
Empty weight 223 kg (492 lb)
Max weight 408 kg (899 lb)
Water ballast None
Max wing loading 17.57 kg/m² (3.6 lb/sq ft)
Max speed 75 kt (139 km/h)
Stalling speed 32 kt (59 km/h)
Best glide ratio 14

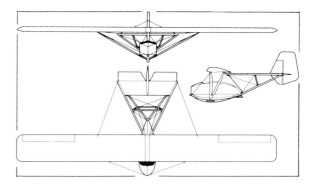

Operation Sigma was set up in 1966 with the object of building a pre-eminent sailplane for the British entry at the 1970 World Championships at Marfa, Texas. Rear Admiral Nick Goodhart was appointed project manager and manufacture of this very high performance sailplane was financially assisted by companies both within and outside the aviation industry. The idea was that Sigma should have two sets of wings: one for thermalling at low speeds with low minimum sink, and the other for good performance at high speeds for cross-country flying. The two wing sections were specially developed for the project by Dr F.X. Wortmann. The aircraft flew for the first time on 12 September 1971 with Nick Goodhart at the controls. Many aspects of handling and performance had been developed to a satisfactory level, but it did not prove possible to overcome difficulties associated with the flaps and flexible closure plates. Sigma's wing consists of a light alloy box structure with full span flaps. These hydraulically operated flaps move in a similar manner to Fowler flaps but the gap between wing and flap is sealed with a flexible closure plate on the lower surface of the wing and spoilers on the upper surface to form a continuous extension of the wing. Each flap carries a full-span trailing edge aileron on the outer panel, and a camber-changing flap on the inner panel. These surfaces remain exposed when the flap is retracted. With the flap extended the circling speed and low sink rate should give a better rate of climb in weak thermals. Forward of the aileron on the upper surface is a light alloy spoiler to assist with lateral control at low speeds. With the flaps retracted the high

rudder incorporates a brake parachute. The tail unit is of light alloy construction with an all-moving T-tailplane incorporating a full-span anti-balance trim tab. The flying controls are all manually operated except for the flaps and the undercarriage, which are hydraulically operated. The hydraulic pressure is achieved by the pilot pushing both rudder pedals back and forth to operate the hydraulic pump. In 1977 the project was taken over by Prof. David J. Marsden of the University of Alberta, who designed and built the Gemini two-seater sailplane. He proposes to replace Sigma's present flaps by simple slotted flaps in the course of his research on variable geometry sailplanes.

Data Sigma 1
Manufacturer Operation Sigma Limited
First flight September 1971
Wing span 21.0 m (68 ft 10¾ in)
Length 8.81 m (28 ft 10¾ in)
Height 1.83 m (6 ft 0 in)
Wing area 12.2 m² (131.3 sq ft)
Wing section Wortmann FX-67 Series
Aspect ratio 36.2
Empty weight 607 kg (1,338 lb)
Max weight 703 kg (1,550 lb)
Water ballast None
Max wing loading 57.6 kg/m² (11.79 lb/sq ft)
Max speed 140 kt (259 km/h)
Stalling speed 37.5 kt (69.5 km/h)
Max rough air speed 110 kt (204 km/h)
Best glide ratio at 63 kt (117 km/h) 48

wing loading and low drag should give a high lift/drag ratio at high speeds. The braking system is operated by lowering the camber-changing flaps and raising the spoilers on the upper surfaces to control the speed.

The fuselage is of the pod and boom type with welded steel tube centre structure faired by the wood framed glassfibre cockpit pod and with the tailboom of light alloy monocoque bolted to it. The long undercarriage is used to ensure that the wing tips have satisfactory ground clearance, necessary due to the large span and the degree of wing flexibility. The retractable sprung tail wheel is mounted in the rudder base and is operated by cables from the main undercarriage. The

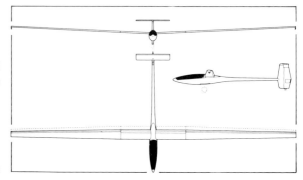

Slingsby T.13 Petrel / United Kingdom

The best-known name among British sailplane manufacturers is undoubtedly that of the late Frederick N. Slingsby. Having served in the Royal Flying Corps in the First World War he helped to found the Scarborough Gliding Club in 1930 and, from repairing the first Primary the club owned, in his furniture works, soon became a designer and builder of gliders. His first glider, the Falcon I, was a version of the Schleicher Falke, built from plans bought from the German Aero Club. In 1932 he developed the Falcon 3 side-by-side sailplane. He eventually moved to Kirbymoorside and produced the Kite, Kadet, Tutor and the Gull, which was the first sailplane to cross the English Channel, from a launch at Dunstable.

The Type 13 Petrel first flew in December 1938 and only six were built before the start of the Second World War. It was an 18-metre span gull-winged version of the successful German Rhönadler, constructed from spruce and birch plywood. It had a low wing loading, suitable for the rather weak thermals encountered in Britain. Initially it was flown with an all-moving tailplane, but later models had a conventional tailplane-with-elevator.

Two are known to be still flying, one in the collection of Mike Russell at Duxford.

Data T.13 Petrel
Manufacturer Slingsby
First flight December 1938
Wing span 17.3 m (56 ft 9 in)
Length 7.25 m (23 ft 9½ in)
Wing area 16.72 m² (180 sq ft)
Wing section Göttingen 535
Aspect ratio 17.9
Empty weight 199 kg (440 lb)
Max weight 289 kg (637 lb)
Water ballast None
Max wing loading 17.3 kg/m² (3.54 lb/sq ft)
Max speed 92 kt (170 km/h)
Stalling speed 25.5 kt (47 km/h)
Min sinking speed at 31 kt (58 km/h) 0.64 m (2.1 ft)/sec
Best glide ratio at 36 kt (67 km/h) 27

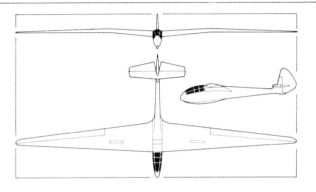

United Kingdom / **Slingsby T.21B**

The T.21, or Sedbergh, has a special place for one generation of British glider pilots. Big, heavy and stable, it was the traditional glider used by clubs and the Air Training Corps for ab initio training for many years. The original T.21 flew for the first time in 1944. There were several initial versions but the T.21B became the standard production model. It was first flown in December 1947 and is still used as an ab initio trainer at some gliding clubs.

This two-seat side-by-side open cockpit glider is of conventional wooden construction and exceptionally simple design. Large areas of fabric covering allow easy access for major inspections and repairs. The high-set braced wings are of single-spar construction with torsion-resisting nose box and a light secondary spar to carry the ailerons. The fuselage is of mixed construction: the forward portion back to the two main wing attachment frames is of wood stressed skin construction; the remainder is of fabric-covered wood girder construction.

The large wheel, robust skid and sprung tail skid provide an undercarriage which is able to stand up to the vagaries implicit in the early training of pilots. Dual flying controls are provided with the spoiler lever and trimmer positioned on the console between the pilots. The spoilers operate only on the wing upper surfaces.

Data T.21B Sedbergh
Manufacturer Slingsby
First flight December 1947
Wing span 16.5 m (54 ft 1½ in)
Length 8.16 m (26 ft 9¼ in)
Wing area 24.2 m² (260.5 sq ft)
Wing section Göttingen 535
Aspect ratio 11.2
Empty weight 267 kg (589 lb)
Max weight 475 kg (1,047 lb)
Water ballast None
Max wing loading 19.6 kg/m² (4.01 lb/sq ft)
Max speed 92 kt (170 km/h)
Stalling speed 28 kt (52 km/h)
Min sinking speed at 33.5 kt (62 km/h) 0.85 m (2.79 ft)/sec
Best glide ratio at 37 kt (69 km/h) 21

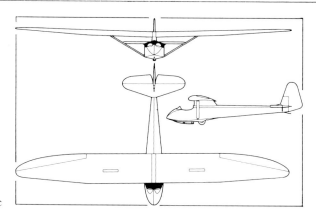

Slingsby T.31 Tandem Tutor / United Kingdom

The Slingsby T.31 Tandem Tutor is still used in large numbers in Britain by the Air Training Corps under the name Cadet 3, where, with the T.21 Sedbergh, they have constituted the standard training gliders for air cadets for many years. Two hundred T.31s have been built since the prototype first flew in September 1950. The low initial cost coupled with the fact that it can easily be flown either solo or dual made this glider an obvious first choice when new gliding clubs were forming in the 1950s.

Based on the single-seat T.8 Kirby Tutor, which first flew in 1937, it uses the same type of wings with wire-braced double struts and the same tail unit. The airframe structure is of wood and is largely fabric covered. Some T.31s have no spoilers but if requested they could be fitted to the wing upper surfaces. The fuselage is a rectangular wood structure, with a plywood-covered forward section and fabric covering on the rear section. The pilots sit in tandem in separate open cockpits in which the flying controls are fully duplicated. A small windscreen is fitted to each cockpit. Landing gear consists of a main wheel, a large bow nose skid and a tail skid.

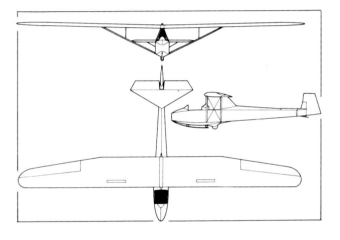

Data   T.31 Tandem Tutor
Manufacturer   Slingsby
First flight   September 1950
Wing span   13.2 m (43 ft 3½ in)
Length   7.1 m (23 ft 3½ in)
Wing area   15.8 m² (170.1 sq ft)
Wing section   Göttingen 426
Aspect ratio   11.0
Empty weight   176 kg (388 lb)
Max weight   376 kg (829 lb)
Water ballast   None
Max wing loading   23.8 kg/m² (4.87 lb/sq ft)
Max speed   70 kt (130 km/h)
Stalling speed   33 kt (61 km/h)
Min sinking speed at 36 kt (67 km/h)   1.05 m (3.44 ft)/sec
Best glide ratio at 39.5 kt (73 km/h)   18.5

United Kingdom / **Slingsby T.34 Sky**

The Sky, a sailplane which must go down in British gliding history for the sheer number of its competition successes alone, won the World Championships in Spain in 1952, flown by the late Philip Wills. Eight T.34 Skys took part and no less than seven were placed in the first fourteen. Skys were placed second in the World Championships of 1954 and 1956.

The T.34 was first referred to as the Gull 5 or 'Slingsby 18 metre' but the name Sky, suggested by John Furlong and incorporating the initials of Slingsby, Kirbymoorside and York, was adopted after the prototype had completed its flight trials. It was developed from the Gull 4 and built at the request of the newly-formed Royal Air Force Gliding and Soaring Association in an attempt to produce a sailplane with a better performance than that of the well-known German Weihe.

Construction of the Sky is of conventional wood and fabric, with a fixed landing wheel. The cockpit is covered by a blown perspex canopy and the rudder pedals are adjustable in flight. The two-piece cantilever wing is fitted with spoilers on the upper surface.

The Sky first flew in 1950 and a total of sixteen were built.

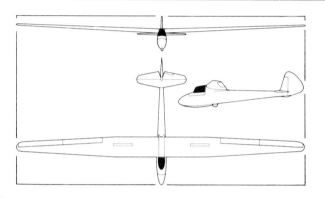

Data   T.34 Sky
Manufacturer   Slingsby
First flight   September 1950
Wing span   18.0 m (59 ft 0½ in)
Length   7.65 m (25 ft 1¼ in)
Wing area   17.37 m² (187 sq ft)
Wing section   Göttingen 547/NACA 2R 12
Aspect ratio   18.7
Empty weight   252 kg (556 lb)
Max weight   363 kg (800 lb)
Water ballast   None
Max wing loading   20.9 kg/m² (4.28 lb/sq ft)
Max speed   98 kt (182 km/h)
Stalling speed   29 kt (54 km/h)
Min sinking speed at 33.5 kt (62 km/h)   0.66 m (2.17 ft)/sec
Max rough air speed   72.5 kt (134 km/h)
Best glide ratio at 37 kt (69 km/h)   27.5

Slingsby T.45 Swallow / United Kingdom

The Slingsby T.45 Swallow is a single-seat glider specifically designed to meet the need for a sailplane to provide solo flying following a two-seater training programme. It is designed not to stall or spin unintentionally even in the hands of an inexperienced pilot, is comparatively robust and has the capacity to absorb a certain amount of rough treatment. Added to this, it has all the features necessary for pilots aiming for their Silver C certificate. The prototype first flew on 11 October 1957 with a 12 m (39 ft 4 in) span wing, but this was changed after initial flight tests to a wing of 13.05 m (42 ft 9¾ in) span.

The cantilever wing is of spruce and plywood construction with a single spar and nose torsion box. Unbalanced wood-framed fabric-covered ailerons are fitted and dive brakes operate above and below each wing. The forward fuselage is a plywood semi-monocoque structure, and the rear section a braced structure of spruce and plywood with fabric-covered sides. The landing gear consists of an unsprung single wheel and rubber-sprung skid. A total of 106 Swallows (not including kits) was built before production was terminated by the fire at Slingsby's Kirbymoorside factory in 1968.

Data T.45 Swallow
Manufacturer Slingsby
First flight October 1957
Wing span 13.05 m (42 ft 9¾ in)
Length 7.04 m (23 ft 1¼ in)
Height 1.58 m (5 ft 2½ in)
Wing area 13.55 m² (145.9 sq ft)
Wing section NACA 63₃618/4412
Aspect ratio 12.6
Empty weight 192 kg (423 lb)
Max weight 318 kg (700 lb)
Water ballast None
Max wing loading 23.47 kg/m² (4.8 lb/sq ft)
Max speed 122.5 kt (227 km/h)
Stalling speed 33.5 kt (62 km/h)
Min sinking speed at 36 kt (67 km/h) 0.76 m (2.49 ft)/sec
Max rough air speed 75 kt (139 km/h)
Best glide ratio at 42.5 kt (79 km/h) 26

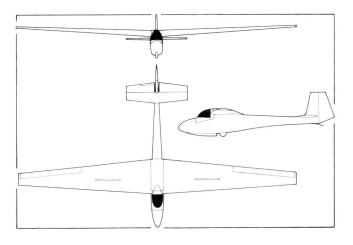

United Kingdom / **Slingsby T.43 Skylark 3**

In the decade from 1955 to 1966 Britain was in the forefront of glider production, with the Skylark 3 series holding many national and international records. Fred Slingsby said that his first Skylark was built for a lark, hence its name. The single-seat Skylark 1, however, of which two were built (both still flying in 1977), was built with a wing span of 13.72 m (45 ft) but with a three-part wing in order to carry out experiments on the outer panels to discover the best type of lateral control surface. The fuselage was based on that of the Slingsby Prefect and it incorporated very effective airbrakes and a canopy. This little sailplane was ahead of its time but it had a very high stalling speed for an era when the demand was for a sailplane to meet the requirements of an average pilot, so modifications were made and the Skylark 2 (upper photo) was produced.

The Skylark 1 was rolled out in March 1953 and the Skylark 2 first flew eight months later. Wing span was increased to 14.63m (48 ft) and a new fuselage of semi-monocoque elliptical section was substituted. Performance was good and the aircraft was found to be a useful addition to club fleets and a stable, highly manoeuvrable acquisition for private owners. A total of sixty-one were built, of which thirty-two had been exported when production ceased in 1962.

To meet the demands of the new generation of young glider pilots Slingsby embarked on an enlarged version of the Standard Class Skylark 2 to result in the 18 metre Skylark 3, which has a larger tail unit. Retaining the three-piece wing of earlier Skylarks the 3B had the cockpit moved forward by 76 mm (3 in), repositioning the centre of gravity to compensate for the larger tail. Although the wing centre section is heavy the Skylark is easy to rig, requiring only four pins to attach the main components and a bolt to secure the tailplane. The wing is constructed from spruce and plywood, with a main spar and a light rear spar, ply covering to the rear spar and fabric covering along the trailing edge. In the Types 3C and 3D these spars were strengthened. Type 3F had geared tabs

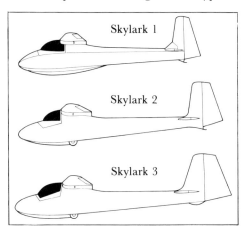

Skylark 1

Skylark 2

Skylark 3

added to the ailerons and the 3G (lower photo) had a longer, narrower aileron without tabs.

The Skylark series uses laminar flow surfaces and is fitted

with airbrakes which operate on both upper and lower wing surfaces. The cockpit provides adequate room for the largest pilot and variations in pilot size are accommodated by an adjustable seat and rudder pedals. Good visibility is provided by the one-piece blown canopy, which hinges sideways.

The landing gear on a few Skylarks consists of a long skid with a jettisonable dolly wheel, but the majority have a fixed landing wheel and nose skid.

A total of 65 Skylark 3s was produced before the type was superseded by the Skylark 4 in 1961.

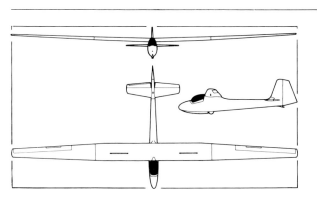

Data T.43 Skylark 3
Manufacturer Slingsby
First flight July 1955
Wing span 18.19 m (59 ft 8¼ in)
Length 7.62 m (25 ft 0 in)
Wing area 16.1 m² (173.3 sq ft)
Wing section NACA 63₃620/4415
Aspect ratio 20.5
Empty weight 248 kg (547 lb)
Max weight 358 kg (789 lb)
Water ballast None
Max wing loading 22.2 kg/m² (4.54 lb/sq ft)
Max speed 116.5 kt (216 km/h)
Stalling speed 31 kt (58 km/h)
Min sinking speed at 35 kt (65 km/h) 0.56 m (1.84 ft)/sec
Best glide ratio at 40 kt (74 km/h) 36

United Kingdom / **Slingsby T.50 Skylark 4**

Although the Type 50 Skylark is structurally a development of the Skylark 3 its new features and fuselage make it virtually a new design. Most striking are the low clean lines with the wing faired directly into the fuselage. The height of the wing is 23 cm (9 in) lower than that of the Skylark 3 and the 18 m (59 ft 0½ in) span wing is almost identical to that of the Skylark 3G except for the modified wing roots. The main spar has been strengthened, cutting out the tendency for the tips to be deflected downwards at speed. First flight of the prototype was in February 1961.

The wings are of all-wood construction with plywood covering to the rear spar and a fabric-covered trailing edge.

Airbrakes are fitted to both upper and lower wing surfaces. The fuselage is a semi-monocoque elliptical section wooden structure and is plywood covered. The landing gear consists of a non-retractable monowheel with rim brake and rubber-sprung skids. The tail unit is conventional, with the fin and tailplane plywood covered and the control surfaces fabric covered.

A total of sixty-three was built and many are still flying. The Skylark achieved some competition success in 1963 when the type won both the US and Canadian National Championships.

Data   T.50 Skylark 4
Manufacturer   Slingsby
First flight   February 1961
Wing span   18.16 m (59 ft 7 in)
Length   7.64 m (25 ft 1 in)
Wing area   16.07 m² (173 sq ft)
Wing section   NACA 63₃620/6415
Aspect ratio   20.5
Empty weight   253 kg (558 lb)
Max weight   376 kg (829 lb)
Water ballast   None
Max wing loading   23.4 kg/m²
(4.79 lb/sq ft)
Max speed   118 kt (219 km/h)
Stalling speed   32 kt (60 km/h)
Min sinking speed at 37 kt (69 km/h)
0.53 m (1.74 ft)/sec
Max rough air speed   71 kt
(132 km/h)
Best glide ratio at 41 kt (76 km/h)
36

Slingsby T.49B Capstan / United Kingdom

The T.49B two-seat sailplane was developed as a successor to the Slingsby Type 42 Eagle to meet a general requirement for a modern training aircraft. Development work began in 1960 and the prototype first flew in November 1961. Full scale production was initiated in the Spring of 1963.

The cantilever high-set wings are of all-wood construction, consisting of a single main spar and plywood leading edge torsion box with fabric covering aft of the spar. The ailerons are plywood covered and dive brakes are fitted to both upper and lower wing surfaces.

The forward fuselage structure consists of spruce frames attached to a central keel box with glassfibre covering. The rear fuselage is a braced wooden girder structure with the bottom skin of plywood and top and sides fabric covered. The landing gear comprises a main skid mounted on a full-length rubber shock absorber and a non-retractable monowheel with band brake. A leaf spring tail skid is also fitted. The two seats are arranged side-by-side in an enclosed cockpit covered by a rearward-hinged one-piece canopy. The tail unit is conventional in configuration, with plywood covered fixed surfaces and fabric covered control surfaces. The Capstan is easy to rig, the wings being attached to each side of the fuselage with three pins. A total of thirty-two Capstans was built.

Data   T.49 Capstan
Manufacturer   Slingsby
First flight   November 1961
Wing span   16.76 m (55 ft 0 in)
Length   8.07 m (26 ft 6 in)
Height   1.58 m (5 ft 2½ in)
Wing area   20.43 m² (220 sq ft)
Wing section   NACA 63₃620/6412
Aspect ratio   13.75
Empty weight   345 kg (761 lb)
Max weight   567 kg (1,250 lb)
Water ballast   None
Max wing loading   27.75 kg/m² (5.68 lb/sq ft)
Max speed   117 kt (217 km/h)
Stalling speed   32.5 kt (60 km/h)
Min sinking speed at 37.5 kt (70 km/h)   0.66 m (2.17 ft)/sec
Max rough air speed   80 kt (148 km/h)
Best glide ratio at 41 kt (76 km/h)   30

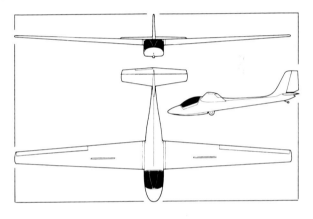

United Kingdom / **Slingsby T.51 Dart 15**

The Dart was the last sailplane to be built by Slingsby in the traditional all-wood manner and indeed was the last model to be designed under the direction of the late Fred Slingsby. The prototype Dart flew for the first time on 26 November 1963, and since then the design has undergone considerable development.

The rear fuselage is long and slim with a small fin and tailplane. The overall length of the fuselage is the same as the length of one wing. The general arrangement and size of the cockpit is the same as that of the Skylark 4, although the fuselage depth is reduced by 10 cm (4 in). This is achieved by running the flying controls along the side of the cockpit

instead of under the pilot's seat. The tailplane is of the all-moving type with anti-balance tabs.

Although graceful in appearance the Dart 15 proved to have a disappointing performance and the manufacturers decided to elongate the wings, thus creating the Dart 17. Some of the modifications, such as using metal spars and root fillets, were adopted to good effect in the production of later Dart 15s. The Standard Class Dart 15 was awarded the OSTIV Design Prize at the 1965 World Championships.

Two Dart 15 Ws (photo) were built for the 1968 World Championships, with a Wortmann wing section and a new cockpit and canopy.

Data T.51 Dart 15
Manufacturer Slingsby
First flight July 1964
Wing span 15.0 m (49 ft 2½ in)
Length 7.47 m (24 ft 6 in)
Wing area 12.63 m² (136 sq ft)
Wing section NACA 64₃618/615
Aspect ratio 17.8
Empty weight 222 kg (489 lb)
Max weight 331 kg (730 lb)
Water ballast None
Max wing loading 24.8 kg/m² (5.08 lb/sq ft)
Max speed 116 kt (215 km/h)
Stalling speed 35 kt (65 km/h)
Min sinking speed at 41.5 kt (77 km/h) 0.67 m (2.2 ft)/sec
Max rough air speed 80 kt (148 km/h)
Best glide ratio at 43 kt (80 km/h) 33.5

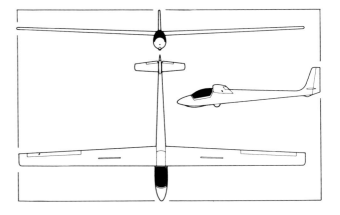

Slingsby T.51 Dart 17 / United Kingdom

When it became apparent that the 15-metre Dart with wooden spar was too heavy for average soaring conditions in Britain, Slingsby added an extra metre to each wing, using detachable wingtips, and thus produced a 17 metre version. However, investigation showed that the spar required modifications to meet the increased stresses and as a result a change to a metal spar was made.

The first Dart 17 with metal spar was rolled out in April 1965. The new wing main spar consists of a single plywood box spar to which light alloy strips have been bonded, two on each side, one at the top and one at the bottom in place of the twin box-section spars. A new trailing edge fillet was added at the wing root to reduce drag and aileron span was increased by 30 cm (11¾ in). The new model was some 16 kg (35¼ lb) lighter than the 15 metre wooden spar version. An optional retractable landing wheel was made available at the end of 1965. This allows a change of wing incidence and thus avoids the tail high attitude of the sailplane when flying at high speeds. This modified version had the suffix R added to its designation. All-metal tailplanes were also fitted on later machines.

Production ended in 1968 after a total of forty-four Dart 17s had been built.

Data T.51 Dart 17R
Manufacturer Slingsby
First flight April 1965
Wing span 17.0 m (55 ft 9¼ in)
Length 7.54 m (24 ft 8¾ in)
Wing area 13.74 m² (148 sq ft)
Wing section NACA 643₃618/615
Aspect ratio 21.0
Empty weight 238 kg (525 lb)
Max weight 370 kg (816 lb)
Water ballast None
Max wing loading 27.0 kg/m² (5.53 lb/sq ft)
Max speed 119 kt (220 km/h)
Stalling speed 35 kt (65 km/h)
Min sinking speed at 40 kt (74 km/h) 0.6 m (1.97 ft)/sec
Max rough air speed 117 kt (216 km/h)
Best glide ratio at 44.5 kt (83 km/h) 36

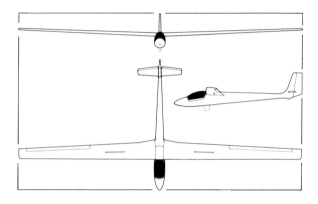

United Kingdom / **Slingsby HP-14C**

The HP-14C is a Slingsby development of the HP-14 high performance single seat sailplane designed by the American R. Schreder. Slingsby had decided to change over from wood to metal when the use of glassfibre or metal was necessary to remain competitive. They took the basic design of Schreder's sailplane and revised it as necessary to meet British requirements.

The V-tail was found to be unsatisfactory for several reasons and it was therefore replaced by a conventional fin with all-moving tailplane. The 17-metre wing span was increased to 18 m and the whole wing moved back 15 cm (6 in) to give a wider centre of gravity range and more roomy cockpit. The flap operating system was completely redesigned: the original rack-and-pinion wind down mechanism was felt to be unsatisfactory since the aerodynamic loads at high speeds made it impossible to apply effectively. A pneumatic system was therefore used, with two jacks to lower the flaps to 90° at VNE, otherwise the flaps are operated manually at normal speeds up to 92 km/hr (50 kt) with the aid of a bungee. The compressed air bottle (at 1,200 lb/sq in) requires recharging after about three operations of the 90° flap position.

The first HP-14C was completed in time for the 1968 World Championships. Three were built before production ceased after the fire at Slingsby in 1968.

Data HP-14C
Manufacturer Slingsby
First flight April 1968
Wing span 18.0 m (59 ft 0½ in)
Length 7.28 m (23 ft 10½ in)
Height 1.19 m (3 ft 11 in)
Wing area 13.58 m² (146.2 sq ft)
Wing section Wortmann FX-61-16
Aspect ratio 23.9
Empty weight 290 kg (639 lb)
Max weight 381 kg (840 lb)
Water ballast None
Max wing loading 28.1 kg/m²
(5.75 lb/sq ft)
Max speed 117 kt (217 km/h)
Stalling speed 29.5 kt (55 km/h)
Min sinking speed at 45.5 kt
(84 km/h) 0.5 m (1.64 ft)/sec
Max rough air speed 104 kt
(193 km/h)
Best glide ratio at 52 kt (96 km/h)
44

Slingsby T.53 / United Kingdom

The T.53 was designed to meet the need for an easily maintained all-metal two-seat trainer for initial or advanced training. Designed by J. Sellars, the original prototype, which first flew on 9 March 1967, had an all-moving tailplane, wing flaps and ailerons of large chord. These were replaced by a conventional fixed tailplane with elevator, the chord of the ailerons was reduced and the flaps were deleted. These changes resulted in a major saving in weight and improved the previously rather high stick forces. The production version, the T.53C, had an extended fin added to the top of the tailplane and the rudder area was increased. The T.53 was Slingsby's first introduction to all-metal

sailplane construction; the decision to change over to all-metal construction was taken because the man hours involved in assembling these aircraft are considerably less than those for wooden ones. Metal is an attractive alternative to wood, being less prone to minor damage and easier and less critical to repair than glassfibre.

Sixteen T.53s were built before production was terminated by the 1968 fire. The T.53 design was later purchased by Yorkshire Sailplanes and the type re-entered production as the YS.53. Three had been built by 1974.

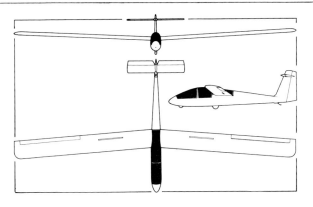

Data T.53C
Manufacturer Slingsby
First flight March 1967
Wing span 17.0 m (55 ft 6 in)
Length 7.7 m (25 ft 3¼ in)
Height 1.83 m (6 ft 0 in)
Wing area 18.02 m² (194 sq ft)
Wing section Wortmann FX-61-184
Aspect ratio 15.9
Empty weight 354 kg (780 lb)
Max weight 580 kg (1,279 lb)
Water ballast None
Max wing loading 32.2 kg/m² (6.59 lb/sq ft)
Max speed 117 kt (217 km/h)
Stalling speed 40.5 kt (75 km/h)
Min sinking speed at 43 kt (80 km/h) 0.76 m (2.5 ft)/sec
Max rough air speed 80 kt (148 km/h)
Best glide ratio at 46 kt (85 km/h) 29

United Kingdom / **Slingsby T.59D Kestrel 19**

After the disastrous fire destroyed Slingsby's Yorkshire factory in September 1968 the financial difficulties which followed resulted in Vickers Ltd taking over the company, which until 1979 traded under the name of Vickers-Slingsby. In September 1969, following the trend of modern sailplane builders, they decided to embark on the production of a glassfibre design. Consequently they entered a licence agreement with Glasflügel of West Germany to build the Kestrel single-seat Open Class sailplane both in its standard 17-metre form and in a 19-metre developed version as the Slingsby T.59D which first flew in July 1971.

Production of Slingsby-built Kestrels began in 1970 and eleven had been delivered (five 17-metre and six 19-metre) by the end of 1971. Slingsby also built a special 19-metre Kestrel, which is designated T.59C and has a carbon-fibre main spar. This aircraft first flew on 7 May 1971.

The wings of the Kestrel 17 were increased to 19 m span on the T.59D by adding half a metre at the wing tips and half a metre at the wing roots. A large fillet was added at the wing roots to reduce drag at low speeds. Other improvements included the introduction of an anti-balance tab on the elevator, giving greater stability, a larger fabric-covered rudder, and the conversion of flaps to flaperons.

Data T.59D Kestrel 19
Manufacturer Slingsby
First flight July 1971
Wing span 19.0 m (62 ft 4 in)
Length 6.6 m (21 ft 7¾ in)
Height 1.47 m (4 ft 9¾ in)
Wing area 12.87 m² (138.5 sq ft)
Wing section Wortmann FX-67-K-170/150
Aspect ratio 28
Empty weight 330 kg (728 lb)
Max weight 472 kg (1,041 lb)
Water ballast 63.6 kg (140 lb)
Max wing loading 36.65 kg/m² (7.51 lb/sq ft)
Max speed 135 kt (250 km/h)
Stalling speed 33 kt (61 km/h)
Min sinking speed at 40 kt (74 km/h) 0.52 m (1.71 ft)/sec
Max rough air speed 105 kt (195 km/h)
Best glide ratio at 52.5 kt (97 km/h) 44

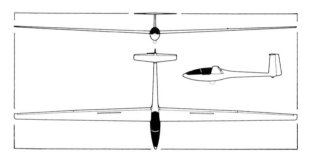

Slingsby T.59H Kestrel 22 / United Kingdom

The T.59H Kestrel 22 is a special version of the single-seat high performance Kestrel 19 and the prototype, which was produced in 1974, was built by using a Kestrel 19 with two 1.5 metre stub wings, complete with flaps, inserted at the wing roots and an extra fin extension mounted above the tailplane. The idea was to make these modifications available to any owner of the Kestrel 19 who wanted to increase the performance of his sailplane, but it was abandoned in favour of a new aircraft, the Kestrel 22. The new four-piece glassfibre wings, with the joint at the flap/aileron junction, incorporate carbon-fibre spars and large Schempp-Hirth airbrakes on both upper and lower surfaces. The fuselage has been lengthened by 750 mm (2 ft 4½ in) by adding a section to the 19 m Kestrel just aft of the wing trailing edge. The tail unit is like that of the Kestrel 19 with the weight of the rudder reduced to prevent flutter by cutting panels out of the glassfibre skin and covering with fabric. Landing gear comprises a large Gerdes monowheel and stout undercarriage. The disc brake is operated by a hydraulic unit coupled to the airbrake system.

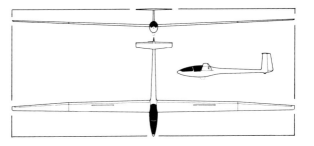

Data T.59H Kestrel 22
Manufacturer Slingsby
First flight 1974
Wing span 22.0 m (72 ft 2 in)
Length 7.55 m (23 ft 9 in)
Height 1.94 m (6 ft 4¼ in)
Wing area 15.44 m² (166.2 sq ft)
Wing section Wortmann FX-67-K-170/150
Aspect ratio 31.35
Empty weight 390 kg (860 lb)
Max weight 659 kg (1,450 lb)
Water ballast 100 kg (220 lb)
Max wing loading 42.68 kg/m² (8.74 lb/sq ft)
Max speed 110 kt (204 km/h)
Min sinking speed at 46 kt (85 km/h) 0.48 m (1.57 ft)/sec
Max rough air speed 105 kt (194.6 km/h)
Best glide ratio at 56 kt (104 km/h) 51.5

Slingsby T.61E Falke / United Kingdom

For many years now most gliding clubs have had at least one two-seat motor glider for training purposes. Use of such an aircraft gives clubs the opportunity of speeding up training, dispensing with winch and retrieve vehicles and of cutting down on ground handling. It also makes possible the continuation of training and indeed of flying at all in weather conditions which would otherwise preclude the launching of motorless sailplanes.

Air Training Corps cadets have so far used the two-seat T.21 Sedbergh and T.31 Tandem Tutor for the limited training they receive; recently, however, there has been a move to equip them with a motor glider and Slingsby have developed the T.61E specifically for this purpose.

The T.61 is a German design originally built by Scheibe as the successful SF-25B and currently built as the SF-25C Falke. It has been built under licence by Slingsby since 1970, and a total of 35 have been completed. The T.61E is an improved version featuring a glassfibre main spar encased in plywood which simultaneously reduces the empty weight and increases the maximum take-off weight. Many other glassfibre components are used in the aircraft, including a new seat designed to improve comfort and to reduce the hazard of loose articles slipping under the seat into the control area.

Data T.61E Falke
Manufacturer Slingsby
First flight April 1977
Wing span 15.3 m (50 ft 2½ in)
Length 7.6 m (24 ft 9 in)
Wing area 17.5 m² (188 sq ft)
Wing section Scheibe
Aspect ratio 13.4
Empty weight 375 kg (827 lb)
Max weight 612 kg (1,349 lb)
Water ballast None
Max wing loading 33.63 kg/m² (6.88 lb/sq ft)
Max level speed 80 kt (148 km/h)
Stalling speed 33 kt (61 km/h)
Min sinking speed 1.0 m (3.28 ft)/sec
Best glide ratio 22
Power plant Rollason-Volkswagen 1,600 cc, 35.8kW (48 hp)
T-O run 200 m (650 ft)

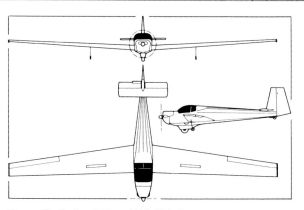

Rate of climb 122 m (400 ft)/min
Range 400 km (216 nm)

Slingsby T.65 Vega / United Kingdom

The Vega is the first wholly Slingsby-designed glassfibre sailplane to appear since the collapse of the original Slingsby company in 1969. One of the main design criteria was the ability to take advantage of the rules governing the 15 m Class, which permit the installation of camber-changing flaps. Designed for optimum performance in its class, the Vega has wings with a flap and airbrake speed-limiting system fitted to their trailing edges and operated by a single control in the cockpit. A sideways movement of the control raises or lowers the flaps ±12° in harmony with the ailerons and changes the camber of the wings. A pull on the lever operates the airbrakes, which are hinged to the flaps with continuous flexible strips.

The cantilever mid-set wings and the tailplane incorporate carbon-fibre spars. The long, slender semi-monocoque fuselage features a comfortable, roomy cockpit, and the one-piece perspex canopy is hinged to open forwards at the nose. Both main and tailwheels are retractable. The first flight was on 3 June 1977. Fifty Vegas has been built by October 1979, and the type has proved itself in several regional and national competitions.

Data Vega
Manufacturer Slingsby
First flight June 1977
Wing span 15.0 m (49 ft 2 in)
Length 6.72 m (22 ft 0½ in)
Wing area 10.05 m² (108.2 sq ft)
Wing section Wortmann FX-67-K-150/FX-71-L-150
Aspect ratio 22.4
Empty weight 234 kg (516 lb)
Max weight 440 kg (970 lb)
Water ballast 88 kg (195 lb)
Max wing loading 43.8 kg/m² (8.97 lb/sq ft)
Max speed 135 kt (250 km/h)
Stalling speed 36 kt (67 km/h)
Min sinking speed at 44 kt (82 km/h) 0.67 m (2.21 ft)/sec
Best glide ratio at 60 kt (111 km/h) 42

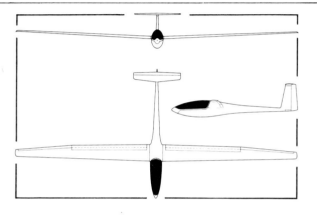

The SD3-15 is a general purpose single-seat 15 metre sailplane designed primarily for clubs and small syndicates. Low capital outlay and running costs have accordingly been combined with safe flying characteristics, low handling weight and small size. Construction of the prototype of this aircraft started in September 1974 and it flew for the first time in March 1975. This aircraft, which is a development of the BG135 designed by J. Gibson, K. Emslie and the late L. Moore, was designated SD3-13V. The prototype is designated SD3-15V (first flight July 1975) and the production aircraft SD3-15T (first flight December 1976), the suffix letter in each case denoting the tail configuration.

The cantilever mid-set wings are built mainly of metal, with metal and polystyrene ribs and wingtips of glassfibre reinforced plastic. The trailing edge airbrakes are all-metal. The fuselage is a semi-monocoque structure of four longerons, metal stressed skin and a nose cone of glassfibre-reinforced plastic. The landing gear consists of a non-retractable monowheel with internally expanding brake.

Data SD3-15T
Manufacturer Swales
First flight December 1976
Wing span 15.0 m (42 ft 2½ in)
Length 6.1 m (20 ft 0 in)
Height 1.30 m (4 ft 3 in)
Wing area 9.57 m² (103 sq ft)
Wing section Wortmann FX-61-168
Aspect ratio 24.0
Empty weight 222 kg (490 lb)
Max weight 330 kg (728 lb)
Water ballast None
Max wing loading 34.48 kg/m² (7.06 lb/sq ft)
Max speed 109 kt (201 km/h)
Stalling speed 35 kt (65 km/h)
Min sinking speed at 42 kt (78 km/h) 0.73 m (2.4 ft)/sec
Max rough air speed 86 kt (159 km/h)
Best glide ratio at 48 kt (89 km/h) 36

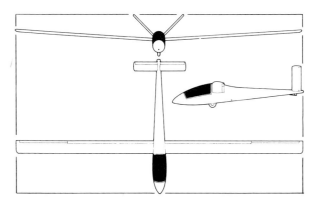

Torva was designed as a moderately priced single-seat sailplane with good performance for use by clubs and private owners. Two versions were designed by John Sellars: the Torva 15 Sprite and the Torva 15 Sport, the former for use as a club sailplane and the latter for recreational and competition flying.

The Torva company made use of the computer-aided Design Centre to draw the fuselage and canopy sections, the aim being to get a good aerodynamic shape and a comfortable cockpit. Glassfibre-reinforced plastic (GRP) was chosen for the construction, with plywood and foam sandwich frames in the fuselage, and plywood ribs in the wings. A specially

modified Wortmann aerofoil was selected to give a good rate of climb in weak British thermals and also to return a stalling speed low enough to permit short-field landings to be made. The wings include airbrakes, and the Torva Sport is fitted with flaps, the first British-designed modern sailplane to be so. The Sprite has provision for water ballast.

The landing gear comprises a sprung main wheel with brake, retractable on the Torva Sport, and a nylon tail wheel. The Torva Sport was first flown on 8 May 1971 by Chris Riddell, who has owned the two existing Torvas since the company closed.

Data Torva 15 Sport
Manufacturer Torva
First flight May 1971
Wing span 15.0 m (49 ft 2½ in)
Length 7.11 m (23 ft 4 in)
Wing area 11.3 m² (121.5 sq ft)
Wing section Modified Wortmann
Aspect ratio 20.0
Empty weight 238 kg (525 lb)
Max weight 408 kg (900 lb)
Water ballast 59 kg (130 lb)
Max wing loading 36.0 kg/m² (7.37 lb/sq ft)
Max speed 116.5 kt (216 km/h)
Stalling speed 35 kt (65 km/h)
Min sinking speed at 43.5 kt (81 km/h) 0.62 m (2.03 ft)/sec
Max rough air speed 80 kt (148 km/h)
Best glide ratio at 44 kt (82 km/h) 37

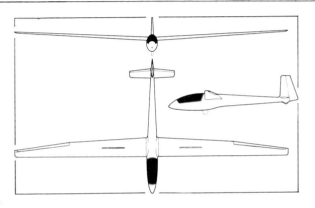

USA / **AmEagle American Eaglet**

The American Eaglet, a single-seat self-launching sailplane of unusual configuration, has been designed by Larry Haig primarily as a glider but with a small single-cylinder engine and enough fuel for a single launch. Cost and weight-saving have strongly influenced the design, and the result is a comparatively inexpensive, docile, easy-to-rig sailplane supplied in kits. Design began in 1974 and the prototype first flew on 19 November 1975.

The fuselage, of the pod and boom type, includes a compact cockpit with side-mounted control stick and aft-hinged, single-curved canopy. The pod consists of a tubular aluminium frame surrounded by a glassfibre shell faired to the 5 in (12.7 cm)-diameter aluminium tailboom, which is bolted to the frame. The rear of the cockpit accommodates a 12 hp (8.95 kW) McCulloch 101B engine driving a two-blade 2 ft (60.96 cm)-diameter pusher propeller. The nylon propeller blades fold aft automatically when the engine stops. The 11 m strutted high wings are constructed of spruce spars and contoured urethane foam covered with pre-moulded glassfibre skins. The inverted V-tail is of similar construction. Spoilers are used for braking and lateral control. The landing gear consists of a semi-retractable monowheel and tailwheels on each tailplane half.

Data American Eaglet
Manufacturer AmEagle
First flight November 1975
Wing span 10.97 m (36 ft 0 in)
Length 4.88 m (16 ft 0 in)
Height 0.91 m (3 ft 0 in)
Wing area 6.69 m² (72.0 sq ft)
Wing section Wortmann FX-61-184
Aspect ratio 18.0
Empty weight 72.5 kg (160 lb)
Max weight 163 kg (360 lb)
Water ballast None
Max wing loading 24.41 kg/m² (5.0 lb/sq ft)
Max speed 100 kt (185 km/h)
Stalling speed 33 kt (61 km/h)
Min sinking speed at 35 kt (65 km/h) 0.76 m (2.5 ft)/sec
Best glide ratio at 45 kt (84 km/h) 27
Powerplant McCulloch 101B, 8.95 kW (12 hp)

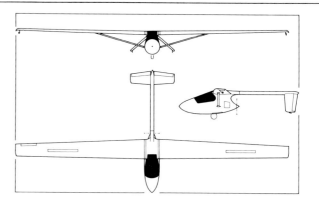

Rate of climb 122 m (400 ft)/min
Fuel capacity 2 lit (0.5 US gal)

The Zuni, named after an American Indian tribe, is the third design from George Applebay and follows his 21 m (68 ft 11 in) Mescalero, which flew in 1975. The Zuni is a single-seat 15 m Class sailplane of glassfibre/foam sandwich construction. The prototype first flew in New Mexico on 18 November 1976; the production machine appeared in 1977 and has since proved to be a good competition sailplane. The fuselage, with swept T-tail, is similar to that of the Mescalero but shorter, and features a roomy cockpit with a semi-reclining seat and in-flight adjustable rudder pedals under a large one-piece canopy. The controls for flaps and landing gear are mounted on the left-hand side of the cockpit, with a side-mounted control stick on the right. The all-moving tailplane is trimmed with a press-button on the control stick.

The two-piece high-set wings contain control linkages which engage automatically when the sailplane is rigged. The interconnecting flaps and ailerons extend the full span of the wings. Flaps can be lowered to +90° for landing or for use as airbrakes. The landing gear consists of a large manually operated retractable monowheel, designed to withstand landings at maximum weight including water ballast, and a tailwheel.

Data Zuni
Manufacturer Applebay
First flight 18 November 1976
Wing span 15.0 m (49 ft 2½ in)
Length 6.71 m (22 ft 0 in)
Height 1.3 m (4 ft 3 in)
Wing area 10.13 m² (109.0 sq ft)
Wing section Wortmann FX-67K-170/150
Aspect ratio 22.2
Empty weight 249 kg (550 lb)
Max weight 544 kg (1,200 lb)
Water ballast 181 kg (400 lb)
Max wing loading 53.7 kg/m² (11.0 lb/sq ft)
Max speed 180 kt (334 km/h)
Stalling speed 34 kt (63 km/h)
Min sinking speed at 43.5 kt (80 km/h) 0.52 m (1.71 ft)/sec

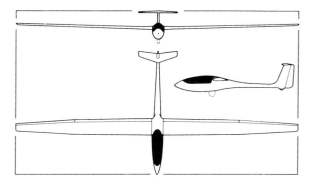

USA / **Bede BD-5S**

The BD-5S is a sailplane version of the BD-5 Micro light aircraft, from which it differs principally in having wings increased in span by 3.17 m (10 ft 5 in), modified landing gear and a revised cockpit layout. A prototype was flown in 1975 and like other members of the BD-5 family it is intended for sale in plan and kit form for amateur construction.

The low-set wings are attached to the fuselage by sliding the tubular spar on to the root section and securing it by two bolts on each side. The wings feature conventional ailerons and four-position flaps which extend for almost the full span of the trailing edges and can be drooped to 60°. The landing gear consists of side-by-side twin main wheels, and nose skid, all fully retractable into the fuselage. The main gear door, which opens forward, also serves as an airbrake. Accommodation consists of a single seat under a detachable framed canopy. An unusual feature is the side-mounted control stick.

Data BD-5S
Manufacturer Bede Aircraft
First flight 1975
Wing span 8.48 m (27 ft 10 in)
Length 4.13 m (13 ft 6¾ in)
Wing area 5.57 m² (60 sq ft)
Wing section NACA 64₁212
Aspect ratio 12.88
Empty weight 102 kg (225 lb)
Max weight 193 kg (425 lb)
Water ballast None
Max wing loading 34.65 kg/m² (7.09 lb/sq ft)
Max diving speed 174 kt (322 km/h)
Stalling speed 34 kt (63 km/h)
Min sinking speed at 43 kt (80 km/h) 0.95 m (3.12 ft)/sec
Best glide ratio 23

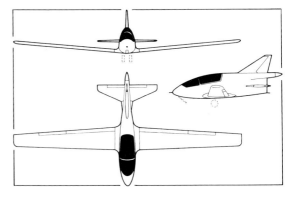

Briegleb BG 12BD / USA

William C. Briegleb built and flew his first glider in 1928, and just before the Second World War he designed the high-wing strutted BG 6 and BG 7. The BG 6 was originally type certificated in 1941 and was used by both civilians and by the US Army Air Corps.

The BG 12 series are single-seat high-performance sailplanes, the prototype of which flew for the first time in 1956. Although the pre-war BG models employed a fabric-covered steel fuselage, the BG 12 series is of conventional wooden construction with ply covering. The wing ribs and fuselage bulkheads are cut from plywood and construction is similar to that of a model aeroplane with spruce longerons covered with ⅛ inch plywood. The trailing edge flaps and ailerons are 1/16 inch ply-covered structures. The conventional tail unit is of wooden construction with ground adjustable tailplane incidence. The landing gear consists of a fixed wheel with Briegleb circumferential brake, and nose skid.

Of the four versions produced, model A is in kit form with a 15% thickness-chord three-piece wing; model B has an 18% section two-piece wing and was developed in 1963; model C is a Standard Class version with airbrakes and model BD is the current version.

Data BG 12BD
Manufacturer Sailplane Corporation of America
First flight July 1973
Wing span 15.0 m (49 ft 1½ in)
Length 6.68 m (21 ft 11 in)
Height 1.22 m (4 ft 0 in)
Wing area 13.1 m² (141 sq ft)
Wing section NACA 4415/4406R
Aspect ratio 17.9
Empty weight 227 kg (500 lb)
Max weight 340 kg (750 lb)
Water ballast None
Max wing loading 25.95 kg/m² (5.31 lb/sq ft)
Max speed 121 kt (225 km/h)
Stalling speed 33 kt (61 km/h)
Min sinking speed at 41 kt (76 km/h) 0.69 m (2.26 ft)/sec
Max rough air speed 112 kt (210 km/h)
Best glide ratio at 45 kt (84 km/h) 33

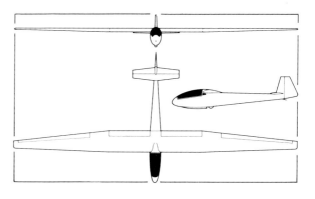

USA / **Briegleb BG 12-16**

In the 1960s William Briegleb developed the single-seat BG 12BR, which Ross Briegleb flew to seventh place in the 1964 National Championships. Later, when the fuselage was damaged in a landing accident it was replaced by a fuselage which had been built for a projected new design, the BG 16. The BG 12-16 is easily recognised by its unusual forward-swept tail unit. It features a low profile fuselage slimmer than that of the BG 12 with a fore section of glassfibre, longer flaps and an all-flying tailplane with two anti-balance servo tabs. The tailplane is of metal construction with glassfibre covering, built in two halves. Construction of the wings is similar to that of the BG 12. The

flaps, ailerons and rudder are of ply-covered wood using spruce and Douglas fir. Accommodation consists of a single semi-reclining seat under a two-piece canopy, the aft section of which is detachable. The landing gear consists of a large non-retractable unsprung monowheel, a shock-absorbing nose skid and sprung tail wheel or tail skid.

The first flight took place in June 1969 and since then many kits have been sold in the USA.

Data   BG 12-16
Manufacturer   Sailplane Corporation of America
First flight   June 1969
Wing span   15.24 (50 ft 0 in)
Length   7.32 m (24 ft 0 in)
Height   1.27 m (4 ft 2 in)
Wing area   13.2 m² (142.1 sq ft)
Wing section   NACA 4415R/4406R
Aspect ratio   17.9
Empty weight   238 kg (525 lb)
Max weight   385 kg (850 lb)
Water ballast   None
Max wing loading   29.17 kg/m² (5.97 lb/sq ft)
Max speed   121 kt (225 km/h)
Stalling speed   29.5 kt (55 km/h)
Min sinking speed at 41.5 kt (77 km/h)   0.68 m (2.23 ft)/sec
Max rough air speed   112 kt (210 km/h)
Best glide ratio at 48.5 kt (90 km/h)   34

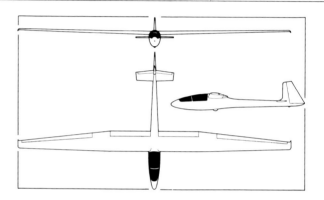

Bryan HP-15 / USA

When it was announced that the 1970 World Championships would take place at Marfa, Richard Schreder was one of many designers who started to plan a new sailplane to take advantage of the Texan climate. Some of the other sailplanes then being designed were the BJ-3, Glasflügel 604, Nimbus 1 and Sigma. Unlike these, the HP-15 was designed to meet the Standard Class rules, which had come into force in 1969, allowing retractable landing gear and fixed hinge flaps on 15-metre sailplanes.

The HP-15 is an all-metal aircraft using an extremely high aspect ratio of 33 and high wing loading to achieve high-speed performance. The two-spar wings contain three ribs in each, the intervening space being filled with plastic foam covered by rolled-to-contour metal skins, with plastic leading edges. Metal flaps and drooping ailerons are used for thermalling and landing. The fuselage is all-metal and incorporated the V-tail characteristic of the HP range. The retractable landing gear is fitted with hydraulic shock-absorbing struts, and the tail wheel is steerable. Like many aircraft which are too advanced for their time, it was found to be difficult to control in flight. It did not participate in the World Championships; neither did it enter production.

Data HP-15
Manufacturer Bryan Aircraft Corporation
First flight Summer 1969
Wing span 15.0 m (49 ft 2½ in)
Length 7.07 m (23 ft 2½ in)
Wing area 6.97 m² (75 sq ft)
Wing section Schreder 69-180
Aspect ratio 33
Empty weight 150 kg (331 lb)
Max weight 272 kg (600 lb)
Water ballast None
Max wing loading 39.0 kg/m² (7.99 lb/sq ft)
Max speed 130 kt (241 km/h)
Stalling speed 30 kt (56 km/h)
Min sinking speed at 39 kt (72 km/h) 0.49 m (1.6 ft)/sec
Max rough air speed 98.5 kt (183 km/h)
Best glide ratio at 47.5 kt (88 km/h) 45

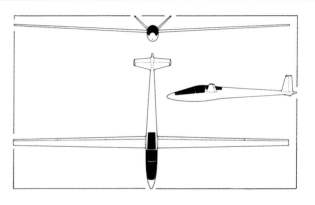

USA / **Bryan HP-18A**

The successful designer and pilot Richard E. Schreder, who designed, built and flew the HP-8 to win the US National Championships in 1958 and 1960, and produced the innovatory HP-10, the HP-11, which was placed third in the 1962 World Championships, and the well-known HP-14 (built in the UK as the HP-14C), is currently producing the Standard Class HP-18 and the HP-18A.

As with many American sailplanes it is sold in kit form for home or club assembly. It is an all-metal aircraft with machined aluminium spars and precut hard foam ribs spaced at 10 cm intervals. A similar rib construction technique is used in the HP-18A, but the spars are of carbon fibre. The fuselage is supplied as a pre-formed Kevlar pod, aluminium body and V-tail. A two-piece flush canopy covers the cockpit.

The cantilever shoulder-set wings feature camber-changing flaps and ailerons running the length of the trailing edge. A retractable landing wheel with brake and a steerable tailwheel comprise the landing gear.

Data HP-18A
Manufacturer Bryan Aircraft Corporation
First flight 1975
Wing span 15.0 m (49 ft 2½ in)
Length 7.16 m (23 ft 0 in)
Height 1.22 m (4 ft 0 in)
Wing area 10.66 m² (114.7 sq ft)
Wing section Wortmann FX-67-150
Aspect ratio 21.1
Empty weight 191 kg (420 lb)
Max weight 417 kg (920 lb)
Water ballast 90 kg (200 lb)
Max wing loading 39.12 kg/m² (8.01 lb/sq ft)
Max speed 130 kt (241 km/h)
Stalling speed 28.5 kt (58 km/h)
Min sinking speed at 39 kt (73 km/h) 0.52 m (1.7 ft)/sec
Max rough air speed 104 kt (193 km/h)
Best glide ratio 40

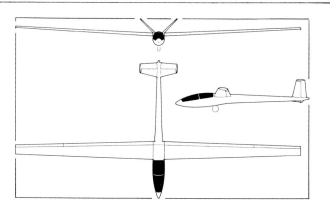

Bryan RS-15 / USA

This 15 metre sailplane was designed by Richard Schreder to meet current OSTIV Standard Class specifications. It is designed for simple, rapid assembly by the homebuilder and is licensed in the amateur-built Experimental category. No jigs are required, and most major components are prefabricated to reduce assembly time to approximately 500 man-hours for a builder with average mechanical aptitude. The cantilever shoulder-set wings are of all-metal construction except for polyurethane foam ribs spaced at 102 mm (4 in) intervals. The wing spar caps are machined from solid aluminium plate. Water ballast is carried inside the wing box spars. The trailing edge flaps/airbrakes are of aluminium sheet bonded to foam ribs. The plain ailerons may be coupled to the flaps. The monocoque fuselage comprises a glassfibre forward pod, complete with bulkheads and moulded seat and a 152 mm (6 in) diameter aluminium tube tailboom with V-tail. Accommodation consists of a single seat under a one-piece Plexiglas canopy. Landing gear is a manually-retractable monowheel and non-retractable tailwheel. Hydraulic shock absorbers are fitted to both the main wheel and tailwheel and a hydraulic brake is fitted to the main wheel.

Data RS-15
Manufacturer Bryan Aircraft Corporation
First flight 1973
Wing span 15.0 m (49 ft 2½ in)
Length 6.71 m (22 ft 0 in)
Height Height 1.17 m (3 ft 10 in)
Wing area 10.5 m² (113 sq ft)
Wing section Wortmann FX-67-K-150
Aspect ratio 21.4
Empty weight 200 kg (441 lb)
Max weight 426 kg (940 lb)
Water ballast 91kg (200 lb)
Max wing loading 40.57 kg/m² (8.31 lb/sq ft)
Max speed 130 kt (241 km/h)
Stalling speed 32.5 kt (60 km/h)
Min sinking speed at 43 kt (80 km/h) 0.64 m (2.1 ft)/sec
Max rough air speed 101 kt (193 km/h)
Best glide ratio 38

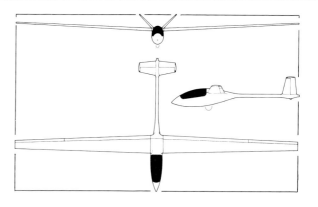

USA / **Concept 70**

Although it has long been apparent that sailplane manufacturers in the USA prefer to build their aircraft from metal, it would be surprising indeed if they had never used glassfibre. In 1970, in fact, Arthur Zimmerman and Wolfgang Schaer produced the first American all-glassfibre sailplane, the Concept 70. This is a single-seat Standard Class sailplane, production of which began in 1973. By the spring of 1974 some sixteen had been built.
The cantilever shoulder-set wings consist of a glassfibre/PVC foam sandwich structure with constant-chord centre section and tapered outer panels. Aluminium flaps on each trailing edge lower to 90°. The glassfibre monocoque fuselage is reinforced with a steel tube frame connecting the landing gear and wing fittings and continuing into the cockpit area to add strength and rigidity. The cockpit itself is roomy and is fitted with a single semi-reclining seat, recessed for an American-type parachute. The one-piece flush Plexiglas canopy is hinged and jettisonable. The manually-retractable Tost monowheel is fitted with a simple drum brake.

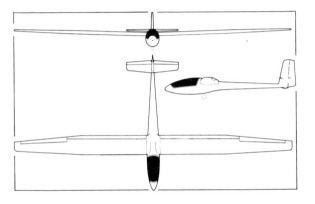

Data Concept 70
Manufacturer Berkshire Manufacturing Corporation
First flight 1970
Wing span 15.0 m (49 ft 2½ in)
Length 7.31 m (24 ft 0 in)
Height 1.83 m (6 ft 0 in)
Wing area 11.52 m² (124 sq ft)
Wing section Eppler/Wortmann
Aspect ratio 20.0
Empty weight 226 kg (500 lb)
Max weight 396 kg (875 lb)
Water ballast 91 kg (200 lb)
Max wing loading 34.38 kg/m² ((7.04 lb/sq ft)
Max speed 105 kt (195 km/h)
Stalling speed 31 kt (58 km/h)
Min sinking speed at 43.5 kt (81 km/h) 0.62 m (2.03 ft)/sec
Max rough air speed 105 kt (195 km/h)
Best glide ratio at 52 kt (96.5 km/h) 40

DSK BJ-1 Duster / USA

The BJ-1 Duster may be said to epitomise gliding as a hobby rather than as a competitive sport. It was designed specifically for amateur construction and no component exceeds 5.5 m (18 ft) so that it can be built in the home and stored in the garage. It was designed by Ben Jansson, an aerodynamicist who captained the Swedish teams in the World Championships at Leszno and Marfa, and by H. Einar Thor, an American aeronautical engineer. The prototype BJ-1 first flew in August 1966 after two-and-a-half years of development.

It is a small all-wood aircraft with three-piece wings incorporating a spruce main spar and trailing edge airbrakes. The fir plywood fuselage shell has a hexagonal cross section at the front and a triangular cross section aft of the wing. Landing gear consists of a main wheel, tail wheel and nose skid.

The BJ-1B is a modified version in which the weight is reduced, the wing span slightly increased and the Plexiglas canopy reduced in height to allow the pilot to sit in a semi-reclining position. Since its introduction, DSK Aviation has supplied more than 200 Duster kits in the USA and throughout the world.

Data BJ-1 Duster
Manufacturer DSK Aviation Corporation
First flight August 1966
Wing span 13.0 m (42 ft 7¾ in)
Length 6.1 m (20 ft 0 in)
Wing area 9.60 m² (103.3 sq ft)
Wing section NACA 4415
Aspect ratio 17.7
Empty weight 159 kg (350 lb)
Max weight 263 kg (580 lb)
Water ballast None
Max wing loading 27.4 kg/m² (5.61 lb/sq ft)
Max speed 111 kt (206 km/h)
Stalling speed 34.5 kt (64 km/h)
Min sinking speed at 67 kt (124 km/h) 1.8 m (5.9 ft)/sec
Max rough air speed 80 kt (148 km/h)
Best glide ratio at 47 kt (87 km/h) 29

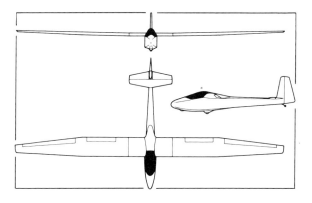

USA / **Laister LP-15 Nugget**

Design and construction of the LP-15 Nugget prototype began in February 1971 by Jack Laister and son Bill, an aerodynamicist. First flight was in June 1971 with certification in mid-1975. Although design work had started in 1970 the manufacturers waited for the CIVV conference on Standard Class requirements before starting construction, leaving only two-and-a-half months for its completion; its maiden flight was also a contest flight.

The cantilever shoulder-set wings are of Chem-Weld bonded aluminium alloy structure and feature long span trailing edge flaps with negative travel (up) for high-speed flight, 8° positive travel (down) for thermalling and 85° positive for landing or use as airbrakes. The top-hinged plain ailerons are of similar construction. The fuselage is a semi-monocoque structure with a forward portion of moulded glassfibre and a rear portion of bonded aluminium alloy which incorporates a cantilever T-tail with slightly swept fin and rudder.

Accommodation consists of a single semi-reclining seat under a fully-transparent two-piece canopy with a removable section and sliding ventilation panel.

Data LP-15 Nugget
Manufacturer Laister
First flight June 1971
Wing span 15.0 m (49 ft 2½ in)
Length 6.1 m (20 ft 0 in)
Height 1.27 m (4 ft 2 in)
Wing area 10.13 m² (109 sq ft)
Wing section Wortmann
Aspect ratio 22.1
Empty weight 210 kg (463 lb)
Max weight 408 kg (900 lb)
Water ballast 84 kg (185 lb)
Max wing loading 40.28 kg/m² (8.25 lb/sq ft)
Max speed 126 kt (233 km/h)
Stalling speed 34 kt (63 km/h)
Max rough air speed 126 kt (233 km/h)
Best glide ratio at 48 kt (89 km/h) 36

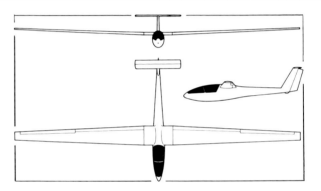

Jack Laister designed and built his first gull-winged aerobatic sailplane in 1938. During the Second World War he worked on the military glider programme and with Mr Kauffmann developed the LK, which was produced in quantity for the military under the designation of TG4A. On July 4 1966 a new single seat high-wing sailplane, the LP-46, was rolled out. It was the prototype of the popular LP-49, familiar to Americans as the 'Forty-Niner'. It is a handsome single-seat Standard Class sailplane with metal laminar flow wings and is designed to be sold in kit form. The extruded aluminium main spar booms are curved in a chordwise direction to follow the aerofoil section, while the roll-contoured sheet aluminium skin is butted and flush riveted with blind pop rivets.

The fuselage is a semi-monocoque structure consisting of two pre-moulded glassfibre halves reinforced with aluminium bulkheads and fittings. The tail unit is a cantilever aluminium structure with sweptback fin and rudder. Landing gear consists of retractable main wheel with brake, glassfibre nose skid with steel shoe, and with non-retractable shrouded tailwheel replacing the retractable wheel of earlier models.

More than 50 kits had been sold by early 1976, and about 35 of these had been completed and flown.

Data LP-49
Manufacturer Laister Sailplanes Inc.
First flight July 1966
Wing span 15.0 m (49 ft 2½ in)
Length 6.28 m (20 ft 7¼ in)
Wing area 13.28 m² (143 sq ft)
Wing section NACA 64₃618
Aspect ratio 17.0
Empty weight 208 kg (460 lb)
Max weight 408 kg (900 lb)
Water ballast None
Max wing loading 30.72 kg/m² (6.29 lb/sq ft)
Max speed 117 kt (217 km/h)
Stalling speed 30 kt (56 km/h)
Min sinking speed at 43 kt (80 km/h) 0.63 m (2.07 ft)/sec
Max rough air speed 117 kt (217 km/h)
Best glide ratio at 50 kt (92.5 km/h) 36.5

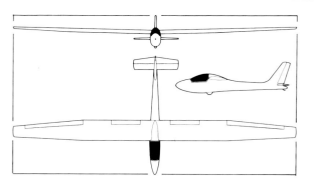

USA / **Maupin Woodstock One**

The Woodstock is a small, simple and inexpensive single-seat wood-and-fabric sailplane for the do-it-yourself builder who has to work to a limited budget. It was designed by Jim Maupin, with advice from Irv Culver, who has designed several sailplanes.

The slender, lightweight fuselage, made of plywood-covered wood, is of hexagonal section forward of the wings and triangular aft. The cockpit accommodates the pilot in semi-reclining position under a single-curved Plexiglas canopy. The shoulder-set cantilever wings are joined by two half-inch (13 mm)-diameter steel pins and secured to the fuselage with three quick-release pins. The wing has a plywood leading-edge D-spar, fabric-covered aft of the spar. Plain, all-wood ailerons are fitted, with upper-surface wooden spoilers for landing control. The wheel is braked by the application of direct pressure to the tyre by means of an aluminium strap activated by a lever on the control column. The tail unit is conventional, with the fin and tailplane plywood-covered and the control surfaces fabric-covered. The whole sailplane can be built on a simple 18 ft (5.5 m)-long trestle and no special jigs or fixtures are needed.

Data   Woodstock One
Manufacturer   Jim Maupin
First flight   Spring 1978
Wing span   11.89 m (39 ft 0 in)
Length   5.43 m (17 ft 10 in)
Height   1.22 m (4 ft 0 in)
Wing area   9.73 m² (104.7 sq ft)
Wing section   Irv Culver
Aspect ratio   14.5
Empty weight   106.5 kg (235 lb)
Max weight   204 kg (450 lb)
Water ballast   None
Max wing loading   20.9 kg/m² (4.3 lb/sq ft)
Min sinking speed   0.79 m (2.6 ft)/sec
Best glide ratio   24

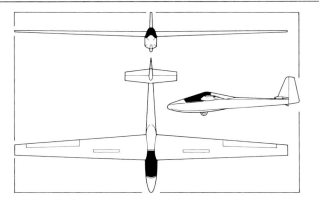

The Tern is a single-seat sailplane with a good performance and simplified construction, designed by Terry Miller for home-builders. Many are under construction in the USA and plans for the aircraft have been sold throughout the world. The Tern 2 is an improved version of the Tern 1, with increased wing span and a drogue parachute fitted in the base of the rudder. The prototype Tern first flew in September 1965, and the Tern 2 made its first flight three years later, in August 1968.

The cantilever shoulder-set wings are of two-piece two-spar construction and are all-plywood covered. Plain all-wood ailerons are fitted and lower-surface wooden spoilers fitted for landing control. The fuselage is a semi-monocoque wooden structure with a glassfibre nose and plywood skin aft of the cockpit. Accommodation comprises a single semi-reclining seat under a three-piece canopy, the centre part of which hinges sideways. The non-retractable landing wheel is located forward of the CG, and there is a skid under the nose. Wheel braking is by the application of direct pressure to the tyre. The tail unit is a conventional cantilever all-wood structure with special hingeline contouring to reduce drag and increase control effectiveness at large deflections.

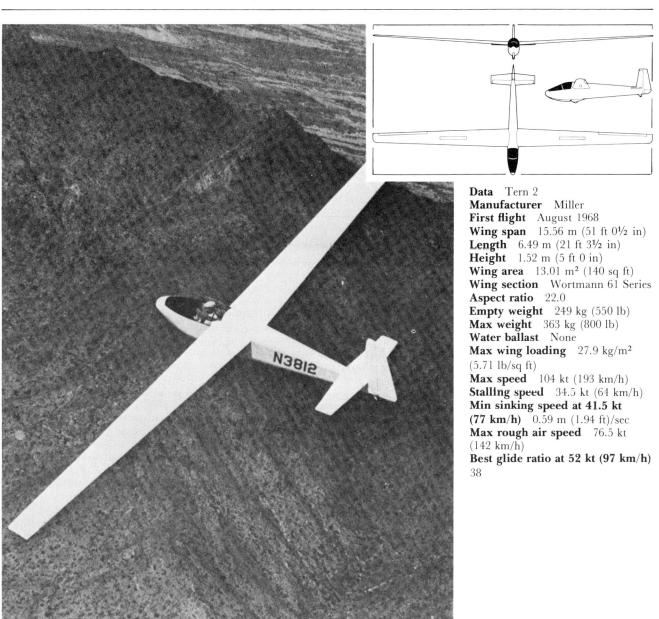

Data Tern 2
Manufacturer Miller
First flight August 1968
Wing span 15.56 m (51 ft 0½ in)
Length 6.49 m (21 ft 3½ in)
Height 1.52 m (5 ft 0 in)
Wing area 13.01 m² (140 sq ft)
Wing section Wortmann 61 Series
Aspect ratio 22.0
Empty weight 249 kg (550 lb)
Max weight 363 kg (800 lb)
Water ballast None
Max wing loading 27.9 kg/m² (5.71 lb/sq ft)
Max speed 104 kt (193 km/h)
Stalling speed 34.5 kt (64 km/h)
Min sinking speed at 41.5 kt (77 km/h) 0.59 m (1.94 ft)/sec
Max rough air speed 76.5 kt (142 km/h)
Best glide ratio at 52 kt (97 km/h) 38

USA / **Monnett Monerai**

The Monerai is one of a new breed of small, light sailplanes available in kit form and benefiting from modern construction methods. Designed and built by John Monnett of Illinois, the prototype flew for the first time in February 1978 with Monnett himself at the controls.

The fuselage is of the pod and boom type, the cockpit being a welded chrome-molybdenum steel tube structure enclosed in a streamlined glassfibre pod; a tubular aluminium tailboom is bolted to the pod. The pilot is accommodated in a reclining sling-type seat, and headrest and rudder pedals are adjustable. The control stick is mounted on the right of the cockpit. On the left a lever operates the trailing-edge flaps, which travel from −8° to +90°. The landing gear consists of a non-retractable monowheel and a tailskid. The constant-chord wing is constructed by bonding aluminium skins to a machined aluminium spar and pressed ribs. Each wing panel weighs only 23.6 kg (52 lb), making rigging easy. Like the wing, the V-tail has pressed aluminium ribs. The all-moving tailplane has its port panel slightly forward of the starboard panel; the two are identical and interchangeable.

There is provision in the basic design for a power unit for self-launching.

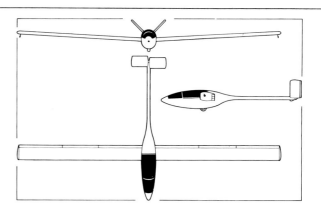

Data Monerai S
Manufacturer Monnett
First flight February 1978
Wing span 11.0 m (36 ft 0 in)
Length 6.0 m (19 ft 7 in)
Height 89 cm (35 in)
Wing area 7.25 m² (78 sq ft)
Wing section Wortmann FX-61192 mod
Aspect ratio 16.6
Empty weight 99.8 kg (220 lb)
Max weight 204.12 kg (450 lb)
Water ballast None
Max wing loading 28.12 kg/m² (5.76 lb/sq ft)
Max speed 104 kt (193 km/h)
Stalling speed 33 kt (61 km/h)
Min sinking speed at 48 kt (89 km/h) 0.85 m (2.8 ft)/sec
Max rough air speed 78 kt (145 km/h)
Best glide ratio at 52 kt (97 km/h) 28

Ryson ST-100 Cloudster / USA

Believed to be the first American motor glider designed for production, the ST-100 has the traditional tractor propeller configuration of the most popular European powered sailplanes. Its design, which was started in March 1974, incorporates many basic advances for this class of aircraft, such as all-metal construction, fully folding wings, power-operated flaps and linked ailerons. Construction of the prototype started in July 1974 and the aircraft flew for the first time on 21 December 1976.

The cantilever low-set wings are of all-metal construction and feature electrically operated trailing edge flaps which are interconnected with the ailerons and operate together from $-12°$ to $+8°$, after which the flaps travel to $+72°$ for braking. The fuselage is a conventional all-metal semi-monocoque structure and incorporates a cantilever T-tail with sweptback fin and rudder and non-swept horizontal surfaces. The two-wheeled main gear and steerable tail wheel are both non-retractable. Accommodation consists of seats for two persons in tandem under a fully transparent one-piece framed canopy which opens sideways.

The Cloudster is powered by a 74.5 kW (100 hp) Continental 0-200 flat-four engine driving a Hoffmann three-position propeller.

Data ST-100 Cloudster
Manufacturer Ryson Aviation Corporation
First flight December 1976
Wing span 17.58 m (57 ft 8 in)
Length 7.78 m (25 ft 6½ in)
Height 1.78 m (5 ft 10 in)
Wing area 19.79 m² (213 sq ft)
Wing section Wortmann FX-67-170/17
Aspect ratio 15.61
Empty weight 550 kg (1,212 lb)
Max weight 748 kg (1,650 lb)
Water ballast None
Max wing loading 37.8 kg/m² (7.74 lb/sq ft)
Max level speed at S/L 130 kt (241 km/h)
Stalling speed 37 kt (69 km/h)
Min sinking speed 0.89 m (2.93 ft)/sec
Best glide ratio 28
Power plant Continental O-200, 74.5 kW (100 hp)

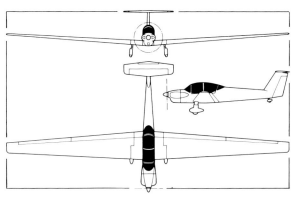

T-O run 174 m (570 ft)
Max rate of climb at S/L 273 m (895 ft)/min
Range 1,103 km (595 nm)

USA / **Schweizer 1-23**

In the early 1930s the Schweizer brothers – Ernie, Paul and Bill – built their first glider, the single-seat SGU 1-1, and in 1935 they formed the Schweizer Aircraft Corporation. During the war they produced military training gliders and diversified into aircraft components. Designs from this period include the 1-19 of 1944, the well-known 2-22 of 1945, the 1-21 of 1947 and the 1-23 of 1948, the last of which won numerous national championships. At this time also American sailplane designers were moving from fabric-covered steel tube frames to all-metal structures comprising monocoque aluminium fuselages and stressed-skin aluminium wings. The 1-23 was one of the first of this type of sailplane to enter series production.

A total of 69 SGS 1-23s of all versions have been produced. The Standard has a wing span of 13.36 m (43.83 ft). In the B, C and D the span was increased to 15.24 m (50.0 ft). The 1-23E, introduced in 1954 with a wing span of 16.09 m (52.8 ft), has a thicker wing skin, and butt joints replace the lap joints on the Type F. The models G and H had a larger fin, and the H-15 has detachable wingtips to meet Standard Class requirements.

In 1961 a 1-23E flown by Paul Bikle set the current world altitude record of 14,102 m (46,267 ft).

Data SGS 1-23D
Manufacturer Schweizer
First flight 1952
Wing span 15.24 m (50.0 ft)
Length 6.25 m (20 ft 4 in)
Height 1.52 m (5 ft 0 in)
Wing area 14.9 m² (160 sq ft)
Wing section NACA 43012A/23009
Aspect ratio 15.6
Empty weight 190 kg (420 lb)
Max weight 340 kg (750 lb)
Water ballast None
Max wing loading 22.8 kg/m² (4.6 lb/sq ft)
Max speed 114 kt (212 km/h)
Stalling speed 28 kt (52 km/h)
Min sinking speed at 30 kt (55 km/h) 0.61 m (1.86 ft)/sec
Best glide ratio at 41.5 kt (77 km/h) 30

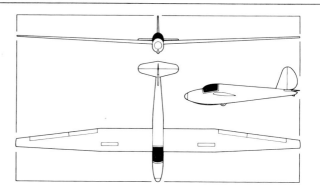

Schweizer 1-26E / USA

This relatively small sailplane was designed for one-design class activities. It was designed to be produced both as a complete sailplane and in kit form for the home-builder. The prototype 1-26 was first flown in January 1954, and with the award of the FAA Type Certificate production of both complete sailplanes and kits began in November of that year. The prototype 1-26 featured a fabric-covered fuselage and wings. The 1-26B, with an all-metal covered wing, flew for the first time in June 1956. The 1-26C was the kit version of the 1-26B and featured the same distinctive elliptical fin. The 1-26D, which first flew in June 1968, had a metal nose section, a re-designed canopy and new fin. The nose was lowered to give the pilot improved visibility and the seat was reclined slightly.

The current production version, the 1-26E, introduces an all-metal semi-monocoque fuselage. The cantilever mid-set wing is an all-metal structure with fabric covered ailerons; balanced airbrakes are fitted immediately aft of the spar on each wing. The landing gear consists of a non-retractable unsprung monowheel with Schweizer brake, aft of a rubber-sprung nose skid, and a small solid rubber tailwheel. More than 700 1-26 sailplanes had been produced by January 1980, of which approximately 200 were in kit form.

Data SGS 1-26E
Manufacturer Schweizer
First flight March 1971
Wing span 12.19 m (40 ft 0 in)
Length 6.57 m (21 ft 6½ in)
Height 2.21 m (7 ft 2½ in)
Wing area 14.87 m² (160 sq ft)
Wing section NACA 430/2A
Aspect ratio 10.0
Empty weight 202 kg (445 lb)
Max weight 318 kg (700 lb)
Water ballast None
Max wing loading 21.39 kg/m² (4.38 lb/sq ft)
Max speed 98.5 kt (183 km/h)
Stalling speed 28.5 kt (53 km/h)
Min sinking speed at 34.5 kt (64 km/h) 0.88 m (2.89 ft)/sec
Max rough air speed 98.5 kt (183 km/h)
Best glide ratio at 46 kt (85 km/h) 23

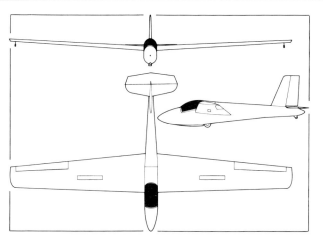

USA / **Schweizer 2-32**

The SGS 2-32 high-performance sailplane has an unusually large cabin capable of carrying one very large or two average-sized passengers in addition to the pilot. The prototype flew for the first time on 3 July 1962. FAA Type Approval was received in June 1964 and production began immediately. More than 88 had been built by January 1977. A number of world and national gliding records have been gained by pilots flying this sailplane. The 2-32 was also chosen to form the basic airframe of the Lockheed YO-3A quiet observation aircraft and the E-Systems L450F.
The cantilever mid-set wings are of all-metal single-spar construction with metal covering; the metal ailerons are fabric covered. Speed limiting spoiler-type airbrakes are fitted to both upper and lower wing surfaces. The tail unit is a cantilever metal structure with all-moving tailplane and adjustable trim tab; control surfaces are fabric-covered. The landing gear consists of a large non-retractable unsprung monowheel with hydraulic brake, a tail skid and sprung wing tip wheels.
The accommodation is arranged beneath a sideways opening blown canopy. The rear control column can be removed for passenger comfort.

Data   SGS 2-32
Manufacturer   Schweizer
First flight   July 1962
Wing span   17.4 m (57 ft 1 in)
Length   8.15 m (26 ft 9 in)
Wing area   16.7 m² (180 sq ft)
Wing section   NACA 63₃618/43012A
Aspect ratio   18.05
Empty weight   385 kg (849 lb)
Max weight   649 kg (1,430 lb)
Water ballast   None
Max wing loading   38.8 kg/m² (7.94 lb/sq ft)
Max speed   122 kt (225 km/h)
Stalling speed   44 kt (81 km/h)
Min sinking speed at 44 kt (80 km/h)   0.72 m (2.38 ft)/sec
Best glide ratio at 51 kt (95 km/h)   34

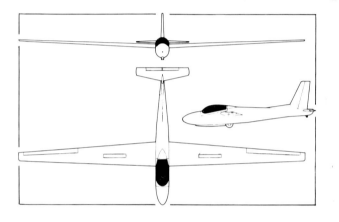

Schweizer 2-33A / USA

The SGS 2-33 was originally developed from the 2-22, with increased wing span and higher performance. The 2-22, with its development B, C, D and E models, was the most popular two-seat training sailplane in America following its introduction in 1948; 258 were built. The prototype 2-33 was first flown in the Autumn of 1966 and received FAA Type Approval in February 1967. Production began in January 1967 and more than 560 2-33s had been built by January 1980; the type is also available in kit form.

The strut-braced high-set wings are of aluminium alloy construction with metal skinning and all-metal ailerons; spoilers are fitted to both upper and lower wing surfaces. The fuselage is a welded chrome-molybdenum steel tube structure with the nose covered with glass-fibre and the remainder being fabric-covered. The landing gear is a non-retractable Cleveland monowheel immediately aft of the nose skid. Wing-tip wheels are also fitted.

The two seats are arranged in tandem beneath a one-piece canopy hinged to the left. The rear pilot has fixed clear panels at the sides and above, and a door on the right.

The 2-33A has become the standard training sailplane in North America and is also exported to other countries.

Data SGS 2-33A
Manufacturer Schweizer
First flight 1966
Wing span 15.54 m (51 ft 0 in)
Length 7.85 m (25 ft 9 in)
Height 2.83 m (9 ft 3½ in)
Wing area 20.39 m² (219.5 sq ft)
Wing section NACA 63₃618
Aspect ratio 11.85
Empty weight 272 kg (600 lb)
Max weight 472 kg (1,040 lb)
Water ballast None
Max wing loading 23.14 kg/m² (4.74 lb/sq ft)
Max speed 85 kt (158 km/h)
Stalling speed 30.5 kt (57 km/h)
Min sinking speed at 33 kt (61 km/h) 0.91 m (2.99 ft)/sec
Best glide ratio at 45.5 kt (81 km/h) 23

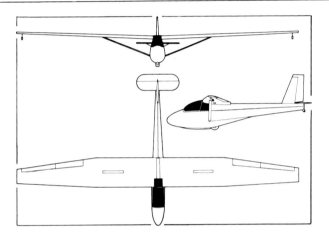

USA / **Schweizer SGS 1-34**

Design of this single-seat high-performance Standard Class sailplane, intended to replace the 1-23 series, began in 1967 and construction of the prototype started in the following year. This flew for the first time in the Spring of 1969 with FAA Type Certification following in September of that year. More than 100 production models had been completed by January 1980.

The cantilever shoulder-set wings are of all-metal aluminium alloy construction with plain all-metal differential ailerons and speed limiting spoiler-type airbrakes fitted both above and below each wing. The fuselage is an all-metal aluminium alloy semi-monocoque structure incorporating a cantilever all-metal tail assembly. The landing gear consists of a non-retractable monowheel with forward skid and auxiliary tailwheel. A retractable monowheel is available as an optional extra.

Accommodation consists of a single seat, with adjustable backrest, beneath a large one-piece canopy.

Data SGS 1-34B
Manufacturer Schweizer
First flight April 1969
Wing span 15.0 m (49 ft 2½ in)
Length 7.85 m (25 ft 9 in)
Height 2.29 m (7 ft 6 in)
Wing area 14.03 m² (151 sq ft)
Wing section Wortmann FX-61-163/60-126
Aspect ratio 16.0
Empty weight 250 kg (550 lb)
Max weight 363 kg (800 lb)
Water ballast None
Max wing loading 25.88 kg/m² (5.3 lb/sq ft)
Max speed 117 kt (217 km/h)
Min sinking speed at 41 kt (76 km/h) 0.64 m (2.1 ft)/sec
Best glide ratio at 45 kt (84 km/h) 34

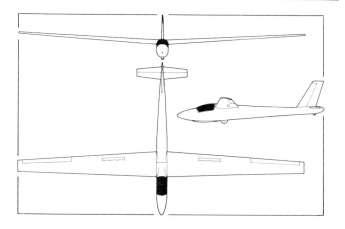

The SGS 1-35 is an all-metal single-seat high-performance 15 metre Class sailplane which was flown for the first time in April 1973. The FAA certification programme was completed in the Spring of 1974. Two versions of the aircraft are available. The 1-35A unrestricted version has a retractable monowheel forward of the centre of gravity and a large tail-wheel; interconnected flaps and ailerons are fitted as standard. The second version is the 1-35C (Club-35), which is a simplified lower cost version for club or syndicate ownership with fixed unsprung monowheel aft of the centre of gravity, nose skid and no water ballast provision. The cantilever shoulder-set wings are of aluminium stressed skin and stringer construction. The bottom-hinged trailing edge flaps and top-hinged ailerons are of aluminium torque cell construction. The fuselage is of all-aluminium monocoque construction and incorporates a cantilever T-tail with fixed incidence tailplane and fabric covered elevator. Later versions of the 1-35A have a more pointed nose and improved wing root fairing.

Accommodation consists of a single semi-reclining seat under a one-piece detachable canopy.

A total of 100 SGS 1-35s of all versions had been produced by January 1980.

Data SGS 1-35A
Manufacturer Schweizer
First flight April 1973
Wing span 15.0 m (49 ft 2½ in)
Length 5.84 m (19 ft 2 in)
Height 1.35 m (4 ft 5 in)
Wing area 9.64 m² (103.8 sq ft)
Wing section Wortmann FX-67-K-170/150
Aspect ratio 23.29
Empty weight 199 kg (440 lb)
Max weight 422 kg (930 lb)
Water ballast 147 kg (323 lb)
Max wing loading 43.78 kg/m² (8.96 lb/sq ft)
Max speed 120 kt (223 km/h)
Stalling speed 35.5 kt (66 km/h)
Min sinking speed at 40 kt (74 km/h) 0.54 m (1.77 ft)/sec
Max rough air speed 120 kt (223 km/h)
Best glide ratio at 54.5 kt (105 km/h) 39

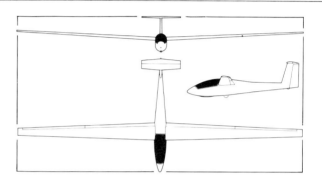

USA / Sisu 1A

The Sisu 1A is one of the most interesting and most successful of American high-performance sailplanes. It is the result of six years of calculation, design and construction by Convair engineer Leonard Niemi, using only a garage as a workshop. The small, elegant and beautifully finished prototype flew for the first time on 20 December 1958. The Sisu is a cantilever shoulder wing metal sailplane featuring a full monocoque wing structure with glassfibre/foam stiffening in the leading edge and camber-changing flaps. The production model, the Sisu 1A, has vented airbrakes and slotted flaps. The slim fuselage terminates in a V-tail and the two-piece canopy provides

excellent visibility. The landing gear consists of a retractable monowheel and a fixed tail wheel.

The Sisu has proved its design by winning the US National Soaring Championships with three different pilots, in 1962, 1965 and 1967. Alvon Parker set three World records in the Sisu, including a flight of 1,041.5 km (562 nm) in 1964. At one time A.J. Smith, US National Champion in 1967, used wing tip extensions to increase the span of his Sisu. The actual Sisu which set the World distance record is now at the Smithsonian Institution.

Data Sisu-1A
Manufacturer Astro Corporation
First flight December 1958
Wing span 15.24 m (50 ft 0 in)
Length 6.46 m (21 ft 2½ in)
Wing area 10.03 m² (108.0 sq ft)
Wing section NACA 65³418
Aspect ratio 23.1
Empty weight 209 kg (460 lb)
Max weight 318 kg (700 lb)
Water ballast None
Max wing loading 31.7 kg/m² (6.49 lb/sq ft)
Max speed 140 kt (260 km/h)
Stalling speed 35.5 kt (68 km/h)
Min sinking speed at 47.5 kt (88 km/h) 0.63 m (2.07 ft)/sec
Max rough air speed 70 kt (130 km/h)
Best glide ratio at 54 kt (100 km/h) 41.4

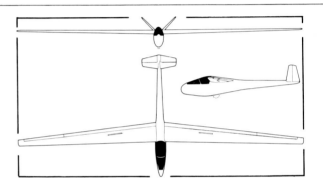

The A-15 is a single-seat Open Class sailplane developed by the Soviet designer Oleg Antonov and his team, who were responsible for the A-11 and A-13, and whose most successful pre-war production was the 'Red Front', which held the women's distance record for 38 years. The A-11 was a single seat sailplane with a wing span of 16.5 m (54 ft 1½ in). Using the fuselage and tail of the A-11 and a new wing of only 12.1 m (39 ft 8½ in) span they developed the A-13, which first flew in May 1958. This sailplane was stressed for aerobatics. About 350 of these two aircraft were built.

The A-15, which first flew in March 1960, signified a considerable advance in Soviet sailplane design. The fuselage, of semi-monocoque construction, is a light aluminium alloy shell, reinforced by frames. The V-tail is of light alloy and the elevators are a mixture of alloy and wood with fabric covering. The aluminium main wing spar is of box section. The Fowler flaps and ailerons of light alloy are filled with plastic foam between the ribs. A 50 litre (13.2 gal) water ballast tank is built into the wing.

In the early 1960s the A-15 set several records, including the World goal distance flight in June 1960 of 714.023 km (385.3 nm), which remained unbroken for three years.

Data   A-15
Manufacturer   Antonov
First flight   March 1960
Wing span   17.0 m (55 ft 9 in)
Length   7.2 m (23 ft 8 in)
Wing area   12.3 m² (132 sq ft)
Wing section   NACA 64₃618/63₃616
Aspect ratio   24
Empty weight   300 kg (661 lb)
Max weight   380 kg (838 lb)
Water ballast   50 kg (110 lb)
Max wing loading   30.89 kg/m² (6.32 lb/sq ft)
Max speed   135 kt (250 km/h)
Stalling speed   29.5 kt (55 km/h)
Min sinking speed at 48.5 kt (90 km/h)   0.63 m (2.07 ft)/sec
Max rough air speed   135 kt (250 km/h)
Best glide ratio at 54 kt (100 km/h)   40

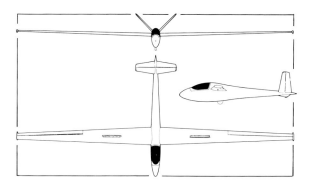

There are two versions of the KAI-14, the all-metal Russian Standard Class sailplane. The first is a competition aircraft with cantilever shoulder wings incorporating inset ailerons, each in two sections, and small trailing edge airbrakes. The leading edges of the wings are swept forward 2° and have a dihedral of 4°. The fuselage, of the pod and boom type, is of metal semi-monocoque construction incorporating a cockpit in which the pilot reclines under a long flush transparent canopy. The landing gear comprises a non-retractable wheel faired into the base of the fuselage, with brake linked with the airbrakes, and a tail skid. The metal surfaces are all highly polished for minimum drag.

The second version of the KAI-14, intended for series production, is similar in structure, but the pilot sits upright in a cockpit covered by a raised canopy and the wetted surfaces are unpolished.

Two KAI-14s were entered in the 1965 World Championships held at South Cerney, England.

Data   KAI-14
Manufacturer   Aviation Institute, Kazan
First flight   Circa 1962
Wing span   15.0 m (49 ft 2½ in)
Length   5.82 m (19 ft 1 in)
Wing area   10.0 m² (107.7 sq ft)
Aspect ratio   22.5
Max weight   260 kg (573 lb)
Water ballast   None
Max wing loading   26.0 kg/m² (5.32 lb/sq ft)
Max diving speed   135 kt (250 km/h)
Landing speed   43.5 kt (80 km/h)
Min sinking speed at 48.5 kt (90 km/h)   0.58 m (1.9 ft)/sec

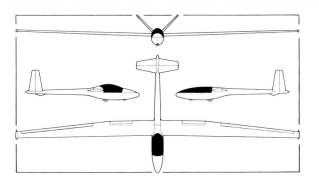

The history of this single-seat sailplane is still somewhat obscure. It is believed to have been designed originally by Balys Karvyalis and first flown, under the designation BK-7, in 1972. It had a Wortmann FX-67-K-170 wing section and a retractable monowheel landing gear, with tailskid. The BK-7, which was of glassfibre construction, was subsequently reported to have entered series production and a Polish journal later referred to a 'BK-7A Lietuva' with a wing span of 20 m (65 ft 7½ in), length of 7.27 m (23 ft 10¼ in), weight of 380 kg (837 lb), best glide ratio of 46 and max speed of 210 km/hr (113 kt). An almost identical aircraft was flown by O. Pasetnik in the Open Class of the June 1976 World Championships in Finland but withdrew from the last two days of the competition because of aileron damage. This aircraft was referred to as the LAK-9 Lietuva and it was reported that the three LAK-9s then built had not, at that time, fully completed flight testing. The LAK-9 is the first Soviet sailplane to compete in the World Championships since 1968.

Data LAK-9 Lietuva
Manufacturer LAK
First flight 1972
Wing span 20.02 m (65 ft 8¼ in)
Length 7.27 m (23 ft 10¼ in)
Height 1.53 m (5 ft 0¾ in)
Wing area 14.99 m² (161.4 sq ft)
Wing section Wortmann FX-67-K-170
Aspect ratio 26.8
Empty weight 380 kg (838 lb)
Max weight 580 kg (1,278 lb)
Water ballast 100 kg (220 lb)
Max wing loading 38.69 kg/m² (7.92 lb/sq ft)
Max speed 121 kt (225 km/h)
Stalling speed 35 kt (64 km/h)
Min sinking speed at 40 kt (74 km/h) 0.51 m (1.67 ft)/sec
Max rough air speed 113 kt (210 km/h)
Best glide ratio at 55.5 kt (103 km/h) 48

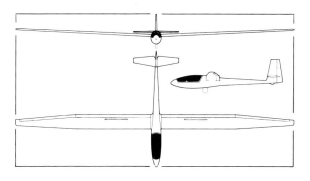

Yugoslavia / **Ikarus Kosava**

An interesting two-seat design of the early 1950s was the Yugoslav Kosava (North Wind). The Yugoslav Flying Sports Organisation commissioned Milos Ilic and Adrýan Kisóvec to design a sailplane to replace the German Kranich. They aimed to produce a two seater with good flying qualities at high speeds and minimum amount of sink at low speeds.

A shoulder-set gull wing was chosen with a slight forward sweep at the leading edge and a marked sweep at the trailing edge. This forward-swept wing was useful for solo flying since it maintained the CG at an acceptable point. The seats were in tandem in a relatively long cockpit. The wing control areas included underwing spoilers, flaps, inner ailerons and outer ailerons. Combining the deflection of flaps and ailerons in various positions made the Kosava suitable for thermalling, cross country and cloud flying. The second prototype featured Schempp-Hirth airbrakes.

The Kosava was built of conventional wood and fabric. The prototype first flew in March 1953, and a few weeks later Bozo Komac achieved victory in the Yugoslav Championships. The Kosava achieved many victories in the two-seater class, taking first place in the World Championships at Camphill 1954 and second place at Saint Yan 1956.

Data Kosava
Manufacturer Ikarus
First flight March 1953
Wing span 19.13 m (62 ft 9 in)
Length 8.33 m (27 ft 4 in)
Wing area 21.12 m² (227.4 sq ft)
Wing section Göttingen 549/CAGI 731-M
Aspect ratio 17.3
Empty weight 336 kg (741 lb)
Max weight 575 kg (1,268 lb)
Water ballast None
Max wing loading 27.2 kg/m² (5.57 lb/sq ft)
Max speed 119 kt (220 km/h)
Stalling speed 29 kt (53 km/h)
Min sinking speed at 40.5 kt (75 km/h) 0.66 m (2.17 ft)/sec
Best glide ratio at 47 kt (87 km/h) 33.5

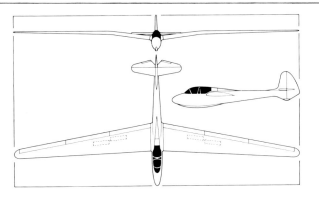

Yugoslav glider manufacturing began as early as 1929, and in 1950 the Orao II achieved a sensational third place in the World Championships held in Sweden. This sailplane was designed by a team of three, Boris Cijan, Stanko Obad and Miho Mazovec, who, in 1954, designed the all-metal Meteor. It is an impressively sleek design and was the precursor of the current breed of slender gliders with camber-changing flaps. The Meteor is a single-seat high performance sailplane with a laminar-flow wing. The fuselage, of semi-monocoque structure, is built in two sections to facilitate repairs. The rear section is straight tapered with stringers and a stressed skin. The cockpit cover is fully detachable. The landing gear comprises an unusually large, retractable bow-shaped front skid and a retractable wheel with brake. The wings have trailing edge flaps, ailerons of which the inner section can be deflected as flaps, and modified DFS airbrakes.

The Meteor was first flown from Belgrade airfield on 4 May 1956 and was soon recognised as a significant high performance sailplane. It attained either fourth or fifth place in the Open Class in the next three World Championships and for a short time held the World speed records for the 100 and 300 km triangles.

Data   Meteor 60
Manufacturer   Ikarus
First flight   May 1956
Wing span   20.0 m (65 ft 7½ in)
Length   8.05 m (26 ft 5 in)
Wing area   16.0 m² (172.2 sq ft)
Wing section   NACA 63₃616 5
Aspect ratio   25.0
Empty weight   376 kg (829 lb)
Max weight   505 kg (1,113 lb)
Water ballast   None
Max wing loading   31.5 kg/m² (6.45 lb/sq ft)
Max speed   135 kt (250 km/h)
Stalling speed   36 kt (67 km/h)
Min sinking speed   0.54 m (1.77 ft)/sec
Max rough air speed   67.5 kt (125 km/h)
Best glide ratio at 48.5 kt (90 km/h)   42

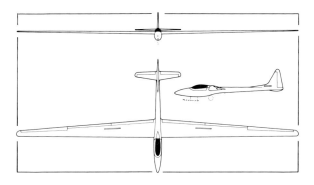

Yugoslavia / **VTC Delfin 3**

The VTC Delfin 1 (photo) made its international debut at the World Championships at South Cerney in England in 1965, but its real impact was felt when it took first and second places in the Polish Nationals in 1966.

This single-seat sailplane was designed by Z. Gabrizel and T. Dragovic of the Aerospace Department, built in the Vrsac factory, and first flew in December 1963. It went into production in quantity as the Delfin 2, in which wooden ailerons replaced those of metal. Twenty-seven were built, four later being converted to Delfin 3s.

The Delfin 3, which was a plywood-covered wooden structure, made its maiden flight in July 1968. The 15 m shoulder-set wings are trapezoid in shape with plywood leading edges and fabric covered rear sections. They include wooden ailerons and metal Schempp-Hirth airbrakes, operating both above and below the wing. The fuselage is a monocoque structure with a wooden tail unit slightly swept back, and a fixed tailplane with elevators, incorporating a trim tab in the starboard side. A feature of the Delfin 3 is the one-piece single curved canopy, which is possible because of the semi-reclining position of the pilot. The landing gear comprises a non-retractable unsprung wheel with brake, a tail skid and a rubber sprung nose skid.

Data Delfin 3
Manufacturer VTC
First flight July 1968
Wing span 15.0 m (49 ft 2½ in)
Length 6.85 m (22 ft 5½ in)
Wing area 12.82 m² (138 sq ft)
Wing section NACA 63₃618
Aspect ratio 17.55
Empty weight 223 kg (492 lb)
Max weight 325 kg (717 lb)
Water ballast None
Max wing loading 25.3 kg/m² (5.18 lb/sq ft)
Max speed 135 kt (250 km/h)
Stalling speed 32.5 kt (60 km/h)
Min sinking speed at 40.5 kt (75 km/h) 0.65 m (2.13 ft)/sec
Max rough air speed 78 kt (145 km/h)
Best glide ratio at 47 kt (87 km/h) 31

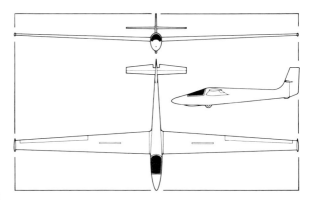

Single-Seaters

Height gain	12,894m (42,303ft)	P F Bikle (USA)	SGS 1 23E	25.2.1961
Absolute height	14,102m (46,266ft)	P F Bikle (USA)	SGS 1 23E	25.2.1961
Straight distance	1,460.8km (907.7ml)	H W Grosse (West Germany)	ASW 12	25.4.1972
Triangular distance	1,063km (660.5ml)	H W Grosse (West Germany) (in Australia)	ASW 17	18.1.1977
Goal and return	1,634.7km (1,015.75ml)	K H Striedieck (USA)	ASW 17	9.5.1977
Goal flight	1,254.26km (779.36ml)	B L Drake, D N Speight (New Zealand)	Nimbus 2	14.1.1978
(Jointly held)		and S H Georgeson		
100km triangle	175km/h (109mph)	K Goudriaan (South Africa)	ASW 17	22.11.1975
300km triangle	153.43km/h (95.3mph)	W Neubert (West Germany) (in Kenya)	Kestrel 604	3.3.1972
500km triangle	143.04km/h (88.9mph)	E Pearson (Gt Britain) (in SW Africa)	Nimbus 2	27.11.1976
750km triangle	141.13km/h (87.69mph)	G Eckle (West Germany) (in S Africa)	Nimbus 2	7.1.1978
1,000km triangle	145.3km/h (90.28mph)	H W Grosse (West Germany) (in Australia)	ASW 17	3.1.1979

Multi-Seaters

Height gain	11,680m (38,320ft)	S Josefczak and J Tarczon (Poland)	Bocian	5.11.1966
Absolute height	13,489m (44,255ft)	L Edgar and H Klieforth (USA)	Pratt-Read G 1	19.3.1952
Straight distance	970.4km (603ml)	I Renner and H Geissler (Australia)	Calif A 21	27.1.1975
Goal and return	751.30km (466.8ml)	E Minghelli and R Gravance (USA)	Prue 2A	26.7.1975
Goal flight	864.86km (537.4ml)	Isabella Gorokhova and Z Koslova (USSR)	Blanik	3.6.1967
100km triangle	147.19km/h (91.56mph)	E Mouat-Biggs and S Murray (S Africa)	Janus	21.11.1977
300km triangle	135.51km/h (84.2mph)	E Mouat-Biggs and S Murray (S Africa)	Janus	16.11.1977
500km triangle	140.06km/h (87mph)	E Mouat-Biggs and S Murray (S Africa)	Janus	17.11.1977

Single-Seaters (Women)

Height gain	9,119m (29,918ft)	Anne Burns (GB) (in South Africa)	Skylark 3B	13.1.1961
Absolute height	12,557.75m (41,199.9ft)	Sabrina Jackintell (USA)	Astir CS	14.2.1979
Straight distance	810km (503.3ml)	Adela Dankowska (Poland)	Jantar 1	19.4.1977
Triangular distance	779.68km (484.2ml)	Elizabeth Karel (Australia)	LS-3	24.1.1979
Goal and return	714.7km (470.37ml)	Hannah Reitsch (West Germany) (in Austria)	St Cirrus	3.6.1978
Goal flight	731.60km (454.6ml)	Tamara Zaiganova (USSR)	A 15	29.7.1966
100km triangle	127.24km/h (79.1mph)	Adele Orsi (Italy)	Kestrel 604	19.8.1975
300km triangle	121.54km/h (75.52mph)	Elizabeth Karel (Australia)	LS-3	30.1.1979
500km triangle	113.9km/h (70.8mph)	Yvonne Leeman (South Africa) (in Rhodesia)	Libelle 301	16.10.1974
750km triangle	73.62km (45.7mph)	Adela Dankowska (Poland)	Jantar 1	2.8.1975

Multi-Seaters (Women)

Height gain	8,430m (27,657ft)	Adela Dankowska and M Mateliska (Poland)	Bocian	17.10.1967
Absolute height	10,809m (35,463ft)	Mary Nutt and H F Duncan (USA)	SGS 2 32	5.3.1975
Straight distance	864.86km (537.4ml)	Tatiana Pavlova and L Filomechkina (USSR)	Blanik	3.6.1967
Goal and return	546km (339ml)	Adele Orsi and M Monti (Italy)	Janus	27.4.1976
Goal flight	864.86km (537.4ml)	Isabella Gorokhova and Z Koslova (USSR)	Blanik	3.6.1967
100km triangle	124km/h (77.05mph)	Adela Dankowska and E Grzelak (Poland)	Halny	1.8.1978
300km triangle	97.74km/h (60.7mph)	Adele Orsi and F Bellengeri (Italy)	Calif A 21	18.8.1974
500km triangle	69.6km/h (43.2mph)	Tamara Zaiganova and V Lobanova (USSR)	Blanik	29.5.1968

FAI World Gliding Championships 1937-1978

1937 International Competition, Wasserkuppe, Germany
(31 pilots took part)

1	Heini Dittmar	Sao Paulo	Germany
2	Ludwig Hofmann	Moazagotl	Germany
3	Wolfgang Spate	Minimoa	Germany

1948 International Competition, Samedan, Switzerland
(28 pilots took part)

1	Per-Axel Persson	Weihe	Sweden
2	Max Schachenmann	Air 100	Switzerland
3	Alwin Kuhn	Moswey 3	Switzerland

1950 International Competition, Örebrö Sweden
(29 pilots took part)

1	Bill Nilsson	Weihe	Sweden
2	Paul McCready	Weihe	USA
3	Maks Borisek	Orao II	Yugoslavia

1952 International Competition, Madrid-Cuatro Vientos, Spain
(39 pilots from 17 countries took part)

1	Philip Wills	Sky	UK
2	Gerard Pierre	Castel-Mauboussin	France
3	Robert Forbes	Sky	UK

Two-seater class

1	Luis Vicente Juez	Kranich 2	Spain
2	Ernst Frowein	Kranich 3	Germany
3	Hanna Reitsch	Kranich 3	Germany

1954 International Competition, Camphill, England
(34 pilots from 19 countries took part)

1	Gerard Pierre	Breguet 901	France
2	Philip Wills	Sky	UK
3	August Wiethücher	Weihe 50	Germany

Two-seater class

1	Rain/Komac	Kosava	Yugoslavia
2	Mantelli/Braghini	Canguro	Italy
3	Smith/Kidder	Schweizer 2-25	USA

1956 International Competition, St Yan, France
(45 pilots from 26 countries took part)

1	Paul McCready	Breguet 901	USA
2	Luis Vicente Juez	Sky	Spain
3	Gorzelak	Jaskolka	Poland

Two-seater class

1	Goodhart/Foster	Eagle	UK
2	Rain/Stepanovic	Kosava	Yugoslavia
3	Sadoux/Bazet	Condor	Argentina

1958 International Competition, Leszno, Poland
Open class (37 pilots from 18 countries took part)

1	Ernst-Günter Hasse	HKS 3	Germany
2	Nicholas Goodhart	Skylark 3	UK
3	Rudolf Mestan	Demant	Czechoslovakia

Standard class (24 pilots from 15 countries took part)

1	Adam Witek	Mucha Standard	Poland
2	Per-Axel Persson	Zugvogel 4	Sweden
3	Heinz Huth	Ka 6	Germany

1960 International Competition, Köln-Butzweilerhof, Germany
Open class (20 pilots from 15 countries took part)

1	Rudolfo Hossinger	Skylark 3	Argentina
2	Edward Makula	Zefir	Poland
3	Jerzy Popiel	Zefir	Poland

Standard class (35 pilots from 22 countries took part)

1	Heinz Huth	Ka 6	Germany
2	George Munch	Ka 6	Brazil
3	Adam Witek	Foka	Poland

1963 International Competition, Junin, Argentina
Open class (25 pilots from 18 countries took part)

1	Edward Makula	Zefir	Poland
2	Jerzy Popiel	Zefir	Poland
3	Richard Schreder	HP 11	USA

Standard class (38 pilots from 23 countries took part)

1	Heinz Huth	Ka 6	Germany
2	Jacki Lacheny	Edelweiss	France
3	Juhani Horma	PIK 16	Finland

1965 International Competition, South Cerney, England
Open class (41 pilots from 27 countries took part)

1	Jan Wroblewski	Foka 4	Poland
2	Rolf Spänig	D-36	Germany
3	Rolf Kuntz	SHK	Germany

Standard class (45 pilots from 25 countries took part)

1	François Henry	Edelweiss	France
2	Markus Ritzi	Std. Elfe	Switzerland
3	Franciscek Kepka	Foka 4	Poland

1968 International Competition, Leszno, Poland
Open class (48 pilots from 27 countries took part)

1	Harro Wödl	Cirrus	Austria
2	Göran Ax	Phoebus C	Sweden
3	Ruedi Seiler	Diamant	Switzerland

Standard class (57 pilots from 24 countries took part)

1	Andrew Smith	Elfe S3	USA
2	Per-Axel Persson	Std. Libelle	Sweden
3	Rudolf Lindner	Phoebus	Germany

1970 International Competition, Marfa, USA
Open class (41 pilots from 25 countries took part)

1	George Moffat	Nimbus	USA
2	Hans-Werner Grosse	ASW 12	Germany
3	Michael Mercier	ASW 12	France

Standard class (44 pilots from 24 countries took part)

1	Helmut Reichmann	LS1	Germany
2	Jan Wroblewski	Cobra 15	Poland
3	Franciszek Kepka	Cobra 15	Poland

1972 International Competition, Vrsac, Yugoslavia
Open class (38 pilots from 21 countries took part)

1	Göran Ax	Nimbus 2	Sweden
2	Mathias Wiitanen	ASW 17	Finland
3	Stanislav Kluk	Jantar	Poland

1972
cont. Standard class (51 pilots from 27 countries took part)

1	Jan Wroblewski	Orion	Poland
2	Eugene Rudensky	ASW 15	USSR
3	Franciszek Kepka	Orion	Poland

1974 International Competition, Waikerie, Australia
Open class (28 pilots from 16 countries took part)

1	George Moffat	Nimbus 2	USA
2	Bert Zegels	604	Belgium
3	Hans-Werner Grosse	ASW 17	Germany

Standard class (38 pilots from 21 countries took part)

1	Helmut Reichmann	LS2	Germany
2	Ingo Renner	Std. Cirrus	Australia
3	Franciszek Kepka	Std. Jantar	Poland

1976 International Competition, Räyskälä, Finland
Open class (39 pilots from 22 countries took part)

1	George Lee	ASW 17	UK
2	J Ziobro	Jantar 2	Poland
3	H Muszcynski	Jantar 2	Poland

Standard class (46 pilots from 25 countries took part)

1	Ingo Renner	PIK-20B	Australia
2	Karlsson	PIK-20B	Sweden
3	George Burton	PIK-20B	UK

1978 International Competition, Chateauroux, France
Open class (24 pilots from 14 countries took part)

1	George Lee	ASW 17	UK
2	Bruno Gantenbrink	Nimbus 2	Germany
3	François Henry	Nimbus 2	France

Standard class (23 pilots from 17 countries took part)

1	Baer Salen	ASW 19	Netherlands
2	Louis Brigliadori	Std. Cirrus	Italy
3	Michel Recule	Cirrus 78L	France

15 m class (32 pilots from 20 countries took part)

1	Helmut Reichmann	SB 11	Germany
2	Karl Striedieck	ASW 20	USA
3	Göran Ax	ASW 20	Sweden

Australia
Schneider ES 52 Kookaburra, 9
Schneider ES 60B Super Arrow, 10
Sutherland MOBA-2C, 11

Austria
Alpla-Werke AVo 68 Samburo, 12
Brditschka HB-3, 13
Brditschka HB-21, 14
Oberlerchner Mg 19, 15
Oberlerchner Mg 23, 16
Standard Austria, 17

Brazil
EEUFMG CB-2 Minuano, 18
IPD Urupema, 19

Canada
Marsden Gemini, 20

Czechoslovakia
LET Blanik, 21
VSO 10, 22

Finland
Eiri PIK-20D, 23
Eiri PIK-20E, 24
Fibera KK-1 Utu, 25
IKV-3 Kotka, 26
PIK-3C Kajava, 27
PIK-16C Vasama, 28

France
Breguet 901, 29
Breguet 905 Fauvette, 30
CARMAM JP.15-36 Aiglon, 31
Fauvel AV.45, 32
Fauvel AV.222, 33
Fauvel AV.361, 34
Fournier RF-9, 35
GEP TCV-03 Trucavaysse, 36
Issoire D 77 Iris, 37
Issoire E 78 Silène, 38
Siren Edelweiss, 39
Wassmer WA 22 Super Javelot, 40
Wassmer WA 28 Espadon, 41
Wassmer WA 30 Bijave, 42

West Germany
Akaflieg Braunschweig SB-9 Stratus, 43
Akaflieg Braunschweig SB-10 Schirokko, 44
Akaflieg Braunschweig SB-11, 45
Akaflieg Darmstadt D-36 Circe, 46
Akaflieg Darmstadt D-39, 47
Akaflieg München Mü 13, 48
Akaflieg München Mü 27, 49
Akaflieg Stuttgart FS-24 Phönix, 50
Akaflieg Stuttgart FS-29, 51
Bölkow Phoebus, 52